LITTLE & Large

Sticker Activity

STICKER TIME

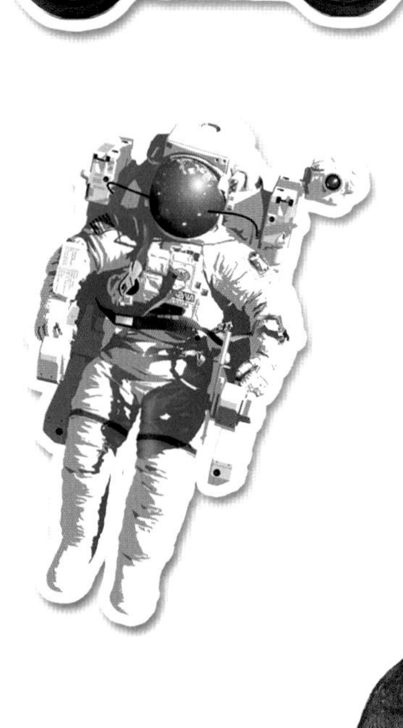

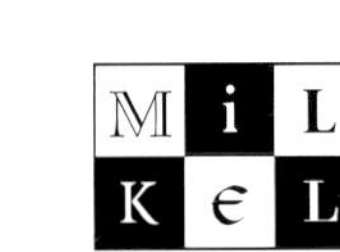

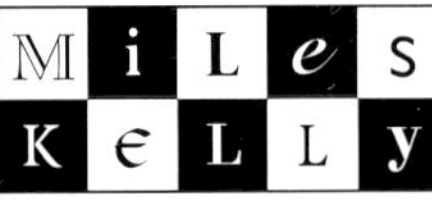

First published in 2006 by Miles Kelly Publishing Ltd
Bardfield Centre, Great Bardfield, Essex, CM7 4SL, UK

This edition published 2010

2 4 6 8 10 9 7 5 3 1

Editorial Director Belinda Gallagher
Art Director Jo Brewer
Assistant Editors Amanda Askew, Lucy Dowling
Designers Louisa Leitao, Tom Slemmings
Cover Designer Simon Lee
Production Manager Elizabeth Brunwin
Reprographics Anthony Cambray, Ian Paulyn
Assets Manager Bethan Ellish

ISBN 978-1-84810-243-9

Printed in China

British Library Cataloguing-in-Publication Data
A catalogue record for this book is available from the British Library

All images from the Miles Kelly Archives

Made with paper from a sustainable forest

www.mileskelly.net
info@mileskelly.net

Space

Space is all around the Earth, high above the air. It is filled with many exciting things such as planets, stars and galaxies.

Today's scientists and astronomers use amazing equipment to discover more about space and the planets in our Solar System. Space shuttles can transport astronauts into space where they carry out important experiments and live on board space stations.

With this great sticker book you can learn all about space and amaze your friends with out of this world facts!

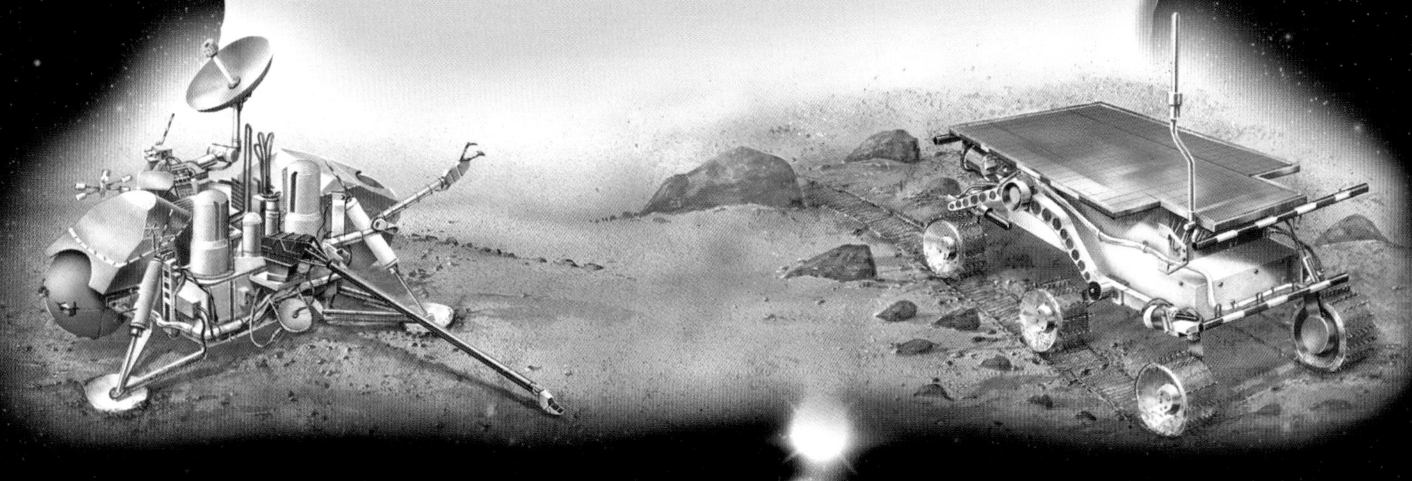

Mini stickers!

Can you name the planets in our Solar System? Which planet is the hottest? What colour are large stars? Use your mini stickers to find out about planets, stars, space travel and how we explore space.

The Solar System – the family of planets that travels around the Sun
The Universe – stars, galaxies and asteroids
Space travel – the exploration of space by astronauts
Looking into space – technology used by scientists to learn more about space

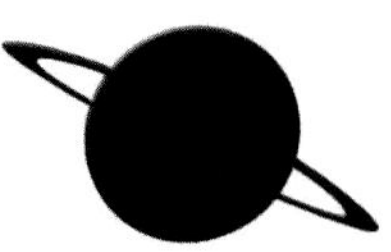

The Solar System

▲ *Earth*

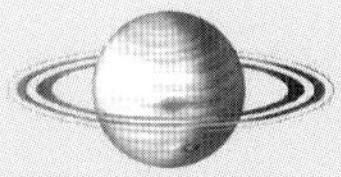

▲ *Neptune*

▲ *Mars*

▲ *Pluto*

▲ *The Moon*

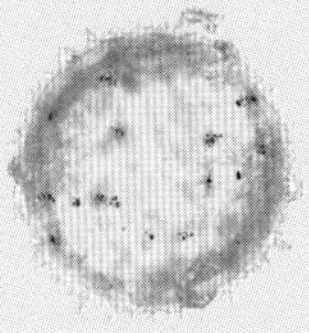

▲ *The Sun*

▲ *Venus*

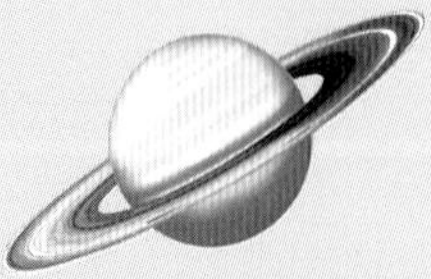

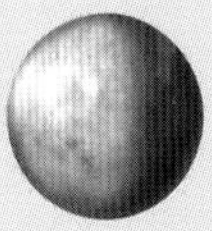

▲ *Mercury*

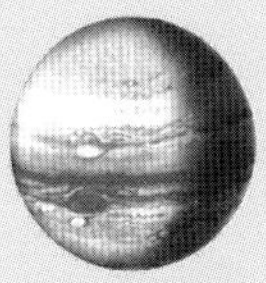

▲ *Jupiter*

▲ *Saturn*

▲ *Uranus*

The Universe

▲ Spiral galaxies

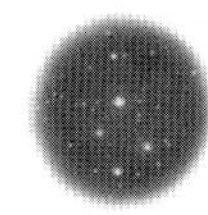

▲ Star cluster

▲ Comet

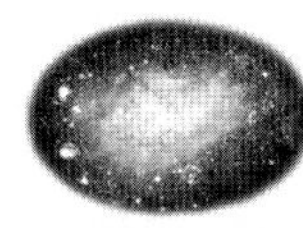

▲ Irregular galaxy

▲ Milky Way

▲ Shooting star

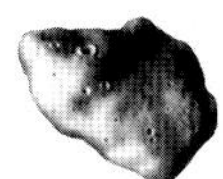

▲ Asteroid

▲ New star

Space travel

▲ Astronaut

▲ International Space Station

▲ Space sleeping bag

▲ Lunar and command modules

▲ Space shuttle

▲ Saturn V

Looking into space

▲ Voyager 2

▲ Satellite telescope

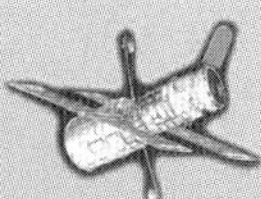

▲ Hubble telescope

▲ Weather satellite

▲ Sojourner rover

▲ Radio telescope

▲ Viking lander

Up in space

★ ▼ *Comet*
A comet is often called a dirty snowball because it is made from dust and ice mixed together

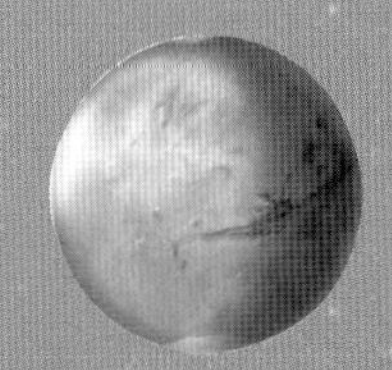

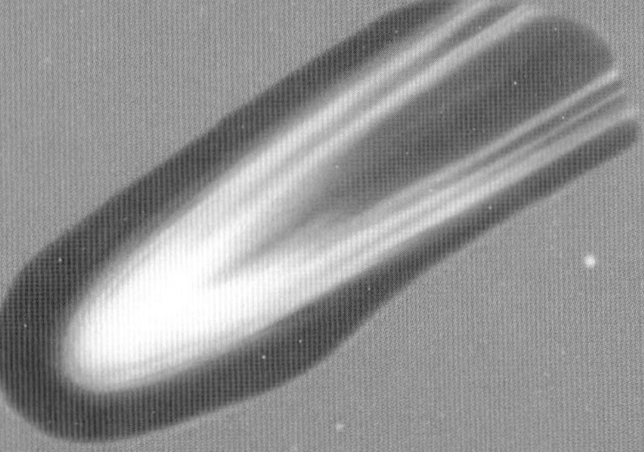

▲ *Mars*
The largest volcano in the Solar System is on Mars

▲ *Astronaut*
Astronauts' space suits protect them from the intense hot or cold and radiation from the Sun

▶ *Earth*
Within our Solar System, Earth is the only planet to support life

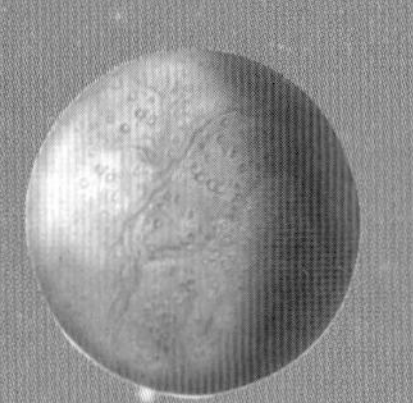

◀ *Pluto*
This is the smallest planet and the farthest from the Sun

▼ *Weather satellite*
This satellite looks down on the clouds and warns of violent storms approaching

▼ *Uranus*
This planet has more moons than any other

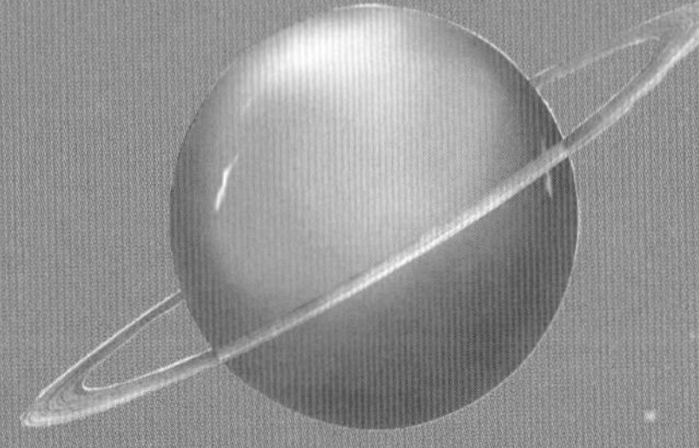

★ ▲ *Spiral galaxies*
These two galaxies are so close that each has pulled a long tail of bright stars from the other

KEY:

The Solar System

The Universe

Space travel

Looking into space

▲ Neptune
Bright blue clouds surround Neptune

▲ Lunar and command modules
These travelled to the Moon joined together, then separated for the Moon landing

▲ Milky Way
The Sun and billions of stars are part of a huge galaxy called the Milky Way

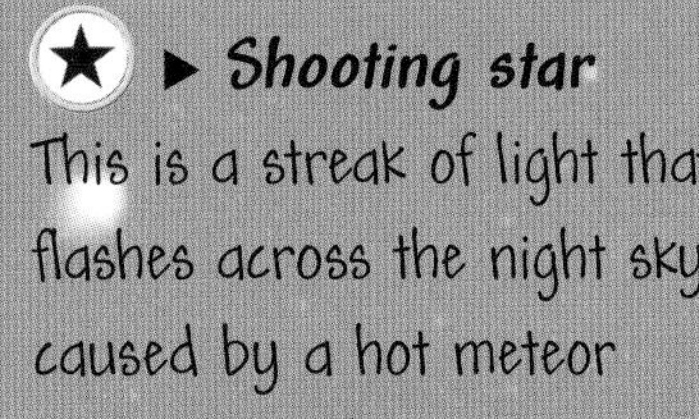

▶ Shooting star
This is a streak of light that flashes across the night sky, caused by a hot meteor racing towards Earth

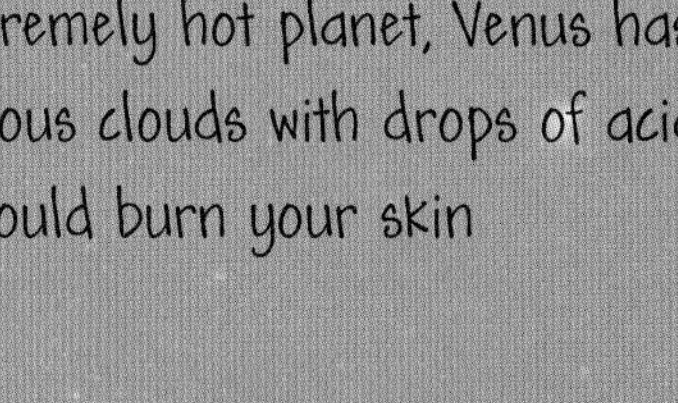

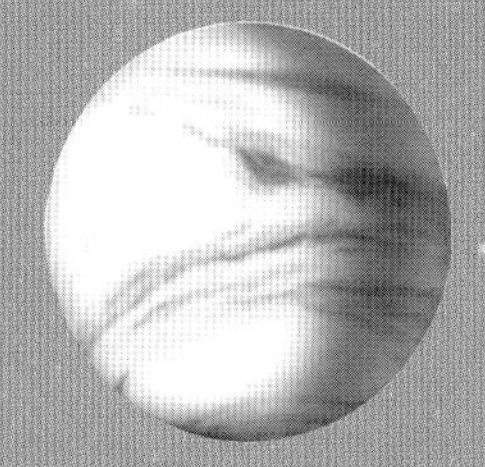

◀ Venus
An extremely hot planet, Venus has poisonous clouds with drops of acid that would burn your skin

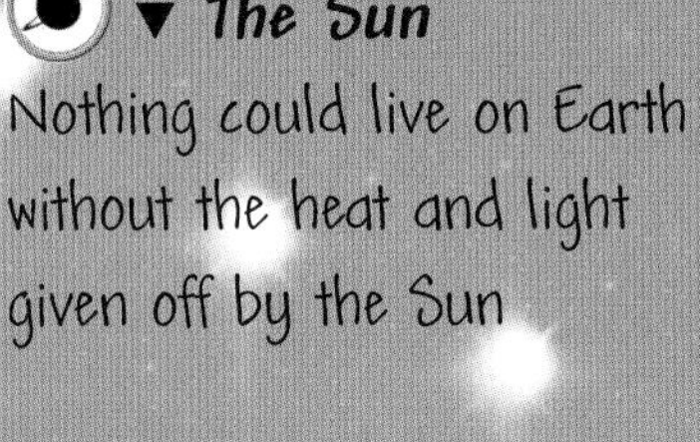

▼ The Sun
Nothing could live on Earth without the heat and light given off by the Sun

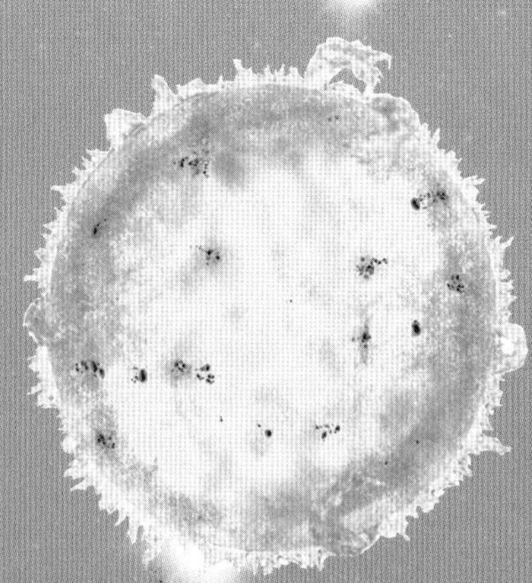

▶ Saturn V
This enormous three-stage rocket carried the spacecraft with the first men to land on the Moon

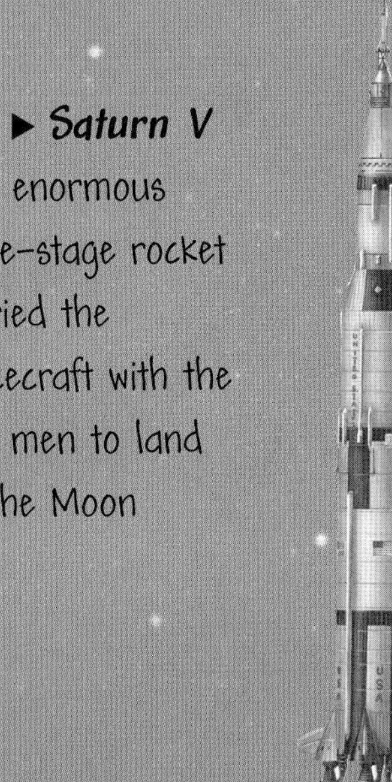

▶ Viking lander
In 1976, two of these space ships touched down on Mars, scraped up some soil and brought it back to Earth for testing

The surface of the Sun is nearly 60 times hotter than boiling water. It is so hot it would melt a spacecraft flying near to it.

Planet Earth

The planet we live on is the Earth. It is a round ball of rock. On the outside the rock is hard and solid. But deep below our feet, inside the Earth, the rock is hot enough to melt. You can sometimes see this hot rock showering out of an erupting volcano.

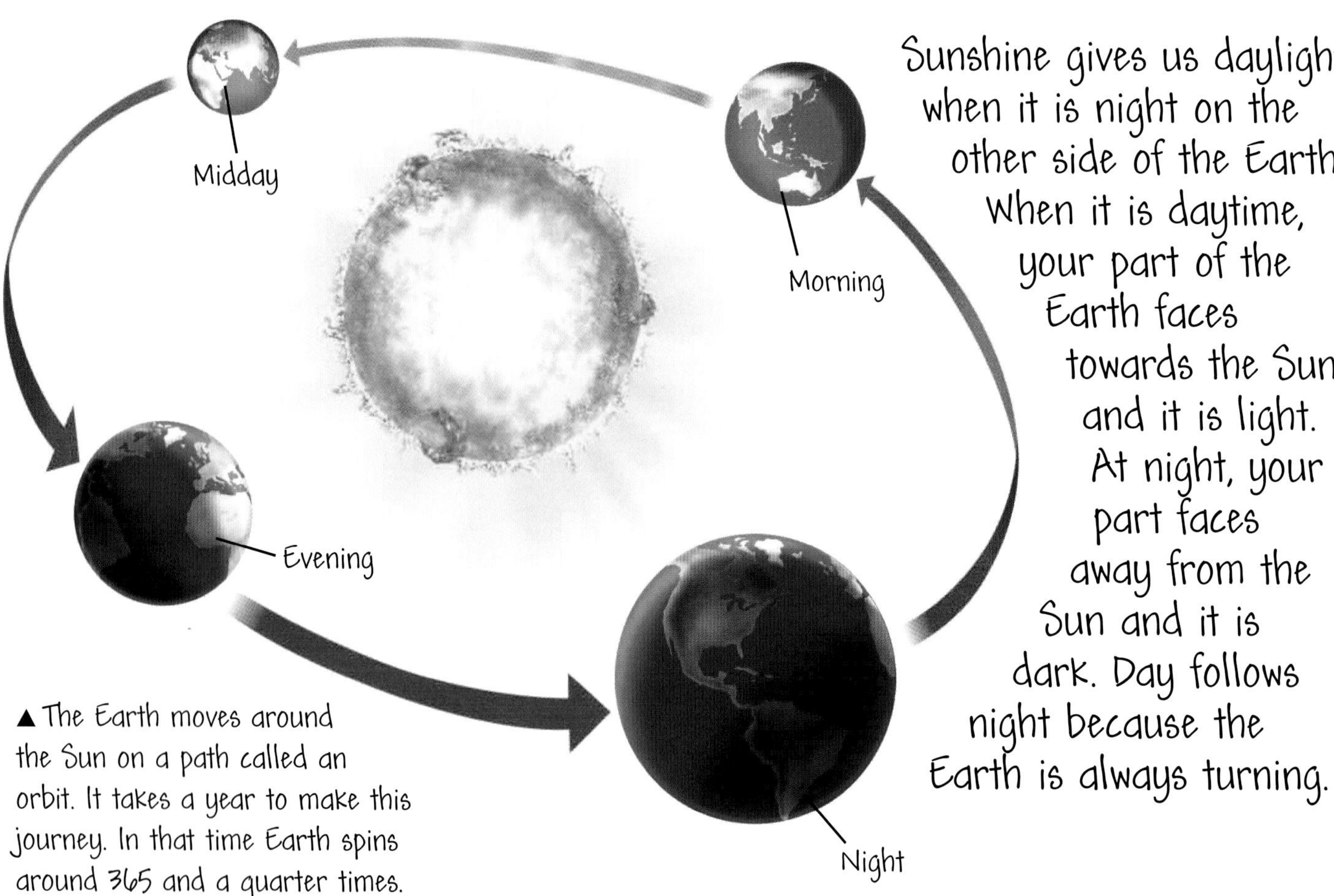

▲ The Earth moves around the Sun on a path called an orbit. It takes a year to make this journey. In that time Earth spins around 365 and a quarter times.

Sunshine gives us daylight when it is night on the other side of the Earth. When it is daytime, your part of the Earth faces towards the Sun and it is light. At night, your part faces away from the Sun and it is dark. Day follows night because the Earth is always turning.

Make a sundial clock

You will need:

• pencil • plasticine • white card • ruler • pen

1. Push the blunt end of the pencil in plasticine and stand it on the centre of the card.
2. Starting in the morning on a sunny day, use a ruler and pen to mark where the shadow of the pencil falls every hour. Write the time next to the line.
3. On the next sunny day, you can use your sundial clock to tell the time (remember, the card must remain in exactly the same spot).

▲ Uranus

▲ Pluto

▲ Comet

▲ Earth

▲ Mars

▲ Astronaut

▲ Weather satellite

▲ Spiral galaxies

Up in space

▶ Uranus

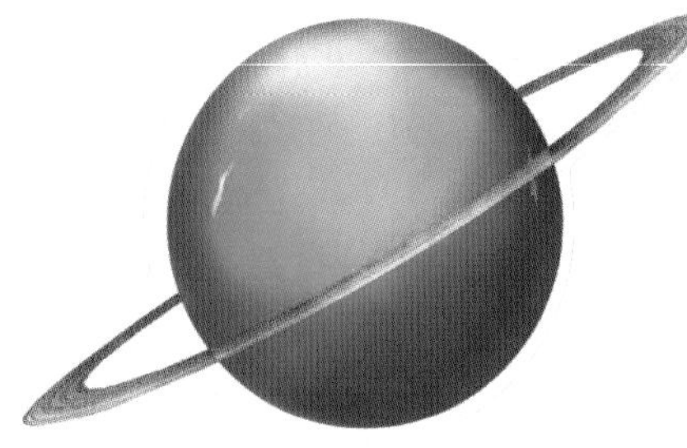

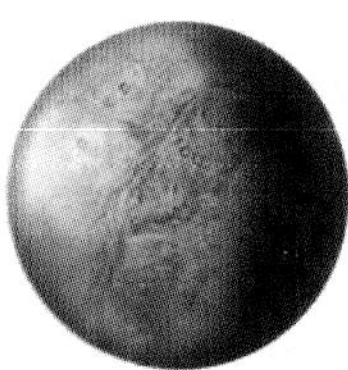

◀ Pluto

▼ Earth

▲ Comet

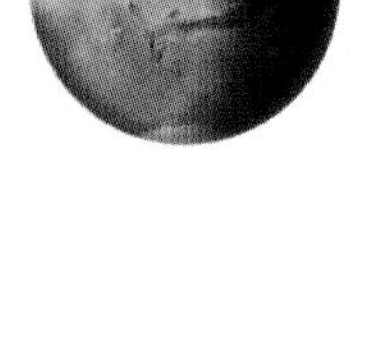

◀ Mars

▲ Astronaut

▶ Weather satellite

◀ Spiral galaxies

Up in space

▲ Milky Way

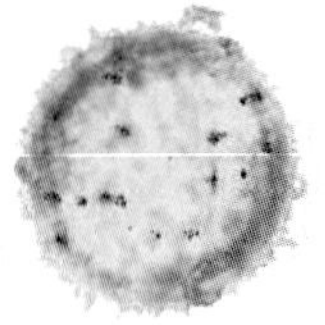
▲ The Sun

▲ Lunar and command modules

▲ Neptune

▲ Shooting star

▲ Viking lander

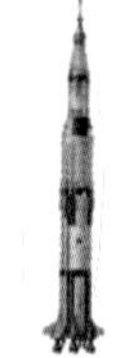
▲ Saturn V

▲ Venus

▲ Milky Way

▼ The Sun
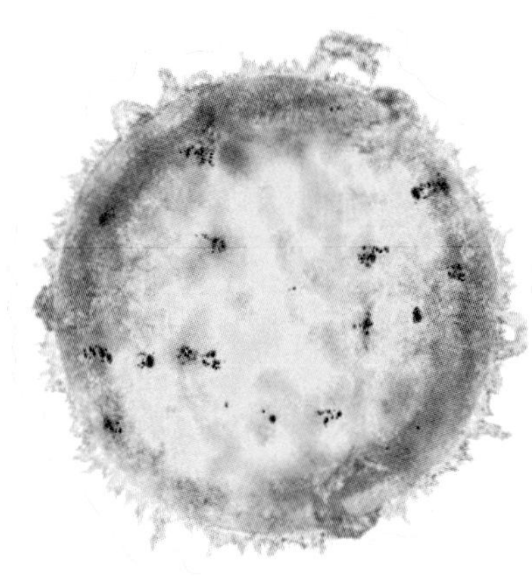

◀ Lunar and command modules

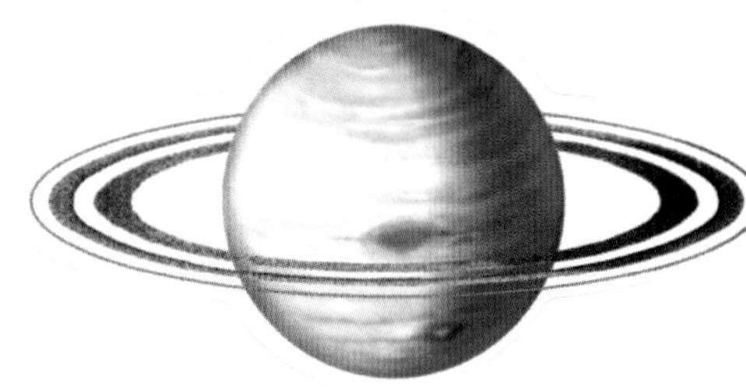
▲ Neptune

▶ Shooting star

◀ Saturn V

▲ Viking lander

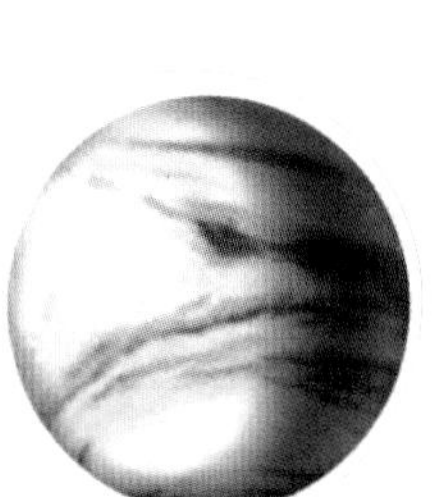
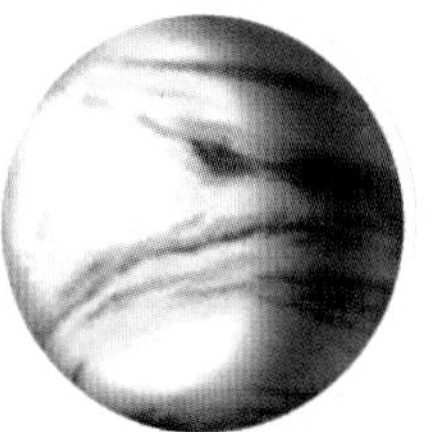
◀ Venus

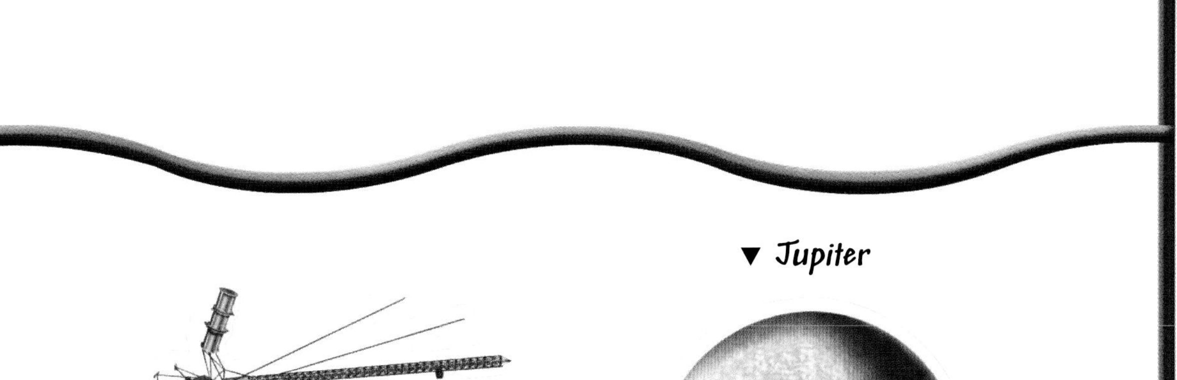

◀ Voyager 2

▼ Jupiter

▶ The Moon

▼ Radio telescope

◀ New star

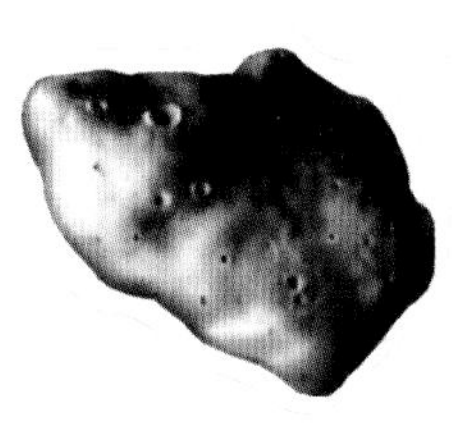

◀ Asteroid

▼ Hubble telescope

▶ Space sleeping bag

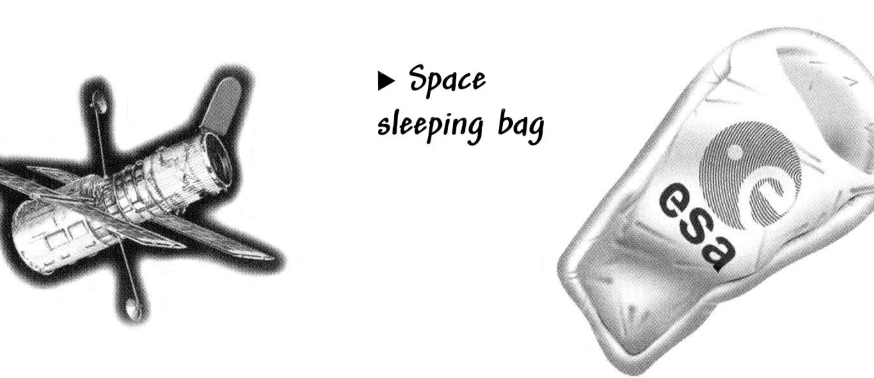

▲ Voyager 2

▲ Jupiter

▲ The Moon

▲ Radio telescope

▲ New star

▲ Asteroid

▲ Hubble telescope

▲ Space sleeping bag

Up in space

▼ International Space Station

▼ Saturn

▼ Star cluster

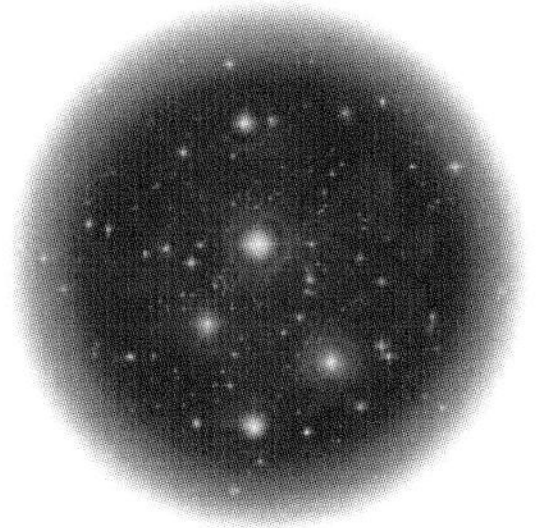

▼ Sojourner rover

► Space shuttle

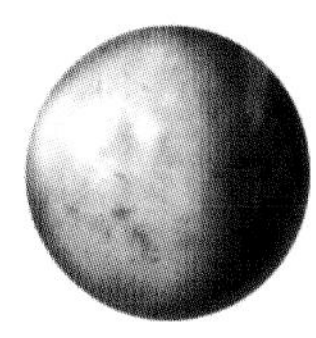

▲ Mercury

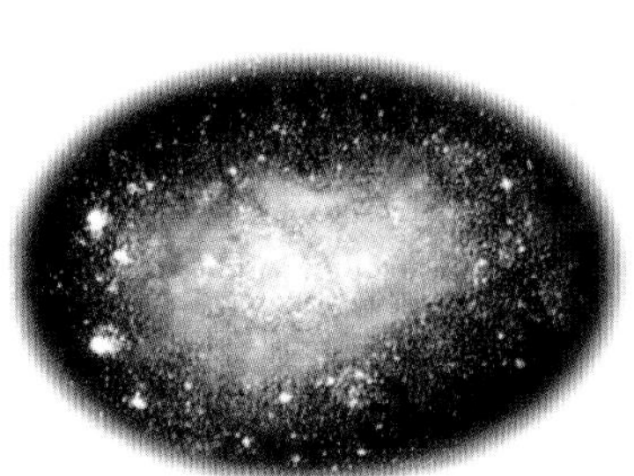

▲ Irregular galaxy

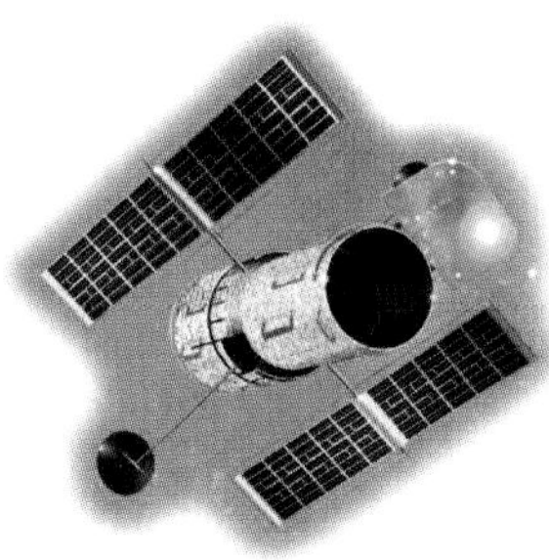

▲ Satellite telescope

▲ International Space Station

▲ Saturn

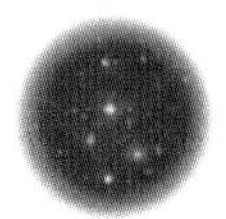

▲ Star cluster

▲ Sojourner rover

▲ Space shuttle

▲ Mercury

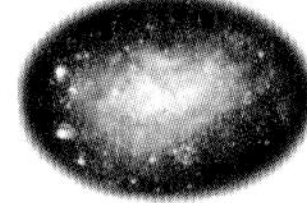

▲ Irregular galaxy

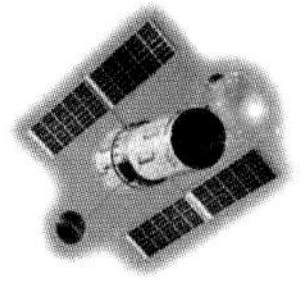

▲ Satellite telescope

Three, two, one ... lift-off!

To blast into space, a rocket has to travel nearly 40 times faster than a jumbo jet. If it goes any slower, gravity pulls it back to Earth. Rockets are powered by burning fuel, which makes hot gases. These gases rush out of the engines, shooting the rocket forwards.

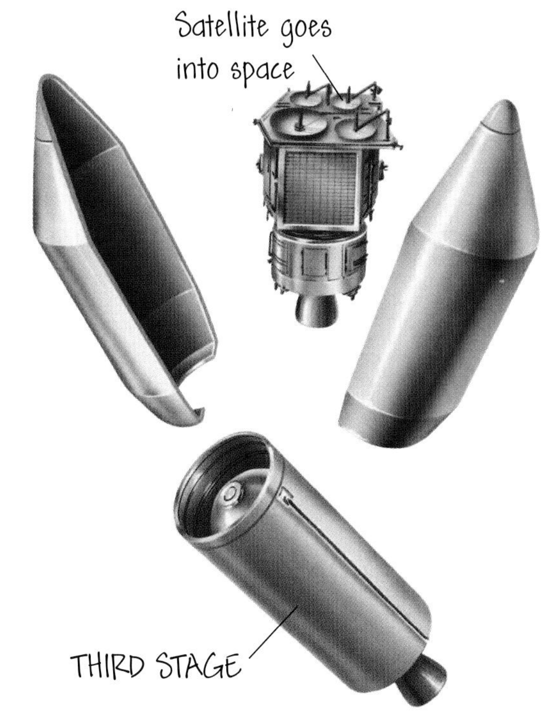

A single rocket is not powerful enough to launch a satellite or spacecraft into space, so rockets usually have two or three main stages. These are separate rockets mounted on top of each other, each with its own engines. When the first stage has used up its fuel it drops away, and the second stage starts. Finally, the third stage takes over taking the satellite into space.

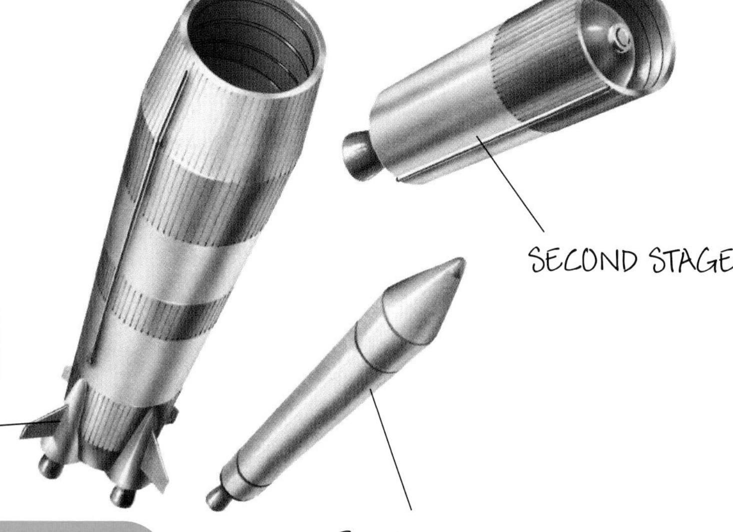

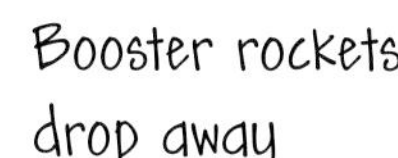

▲ Each stage fires its engines to make the rocket go faster and faster until it releases the satellite into space.

Make a Moon calendar

You will need:

• sheet of paper • coloured pencils • ruler

1. Divide the sheet of paper into squares for the days of the month.
2. Each night, draw the shape of the Moon as you see it from your window. If it is cloudy and you cannot see the Moon just draw clouds.
3. After a month you will have a complete record of the changing view of the Moon.

Up in space

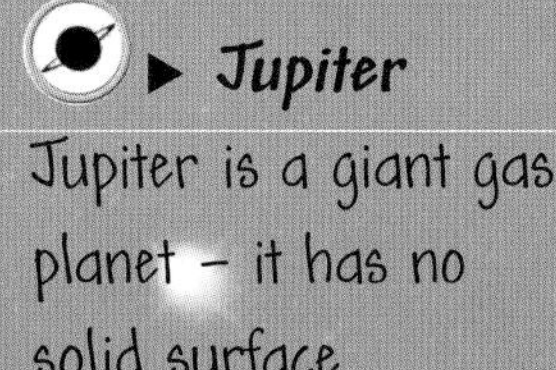

▶ Jupiter

Jupiter is a giant gas planet – it has no solid surface

▲ Space sleeping bag

Everything floats around in space! Space sleeping bags need to be fixed to a wall to stop sleeping astronauts bumping into things!

◀ Voyager 2

In 1977 this probe sent back thousands of pictures of Uranus and Neptune as it flew past them

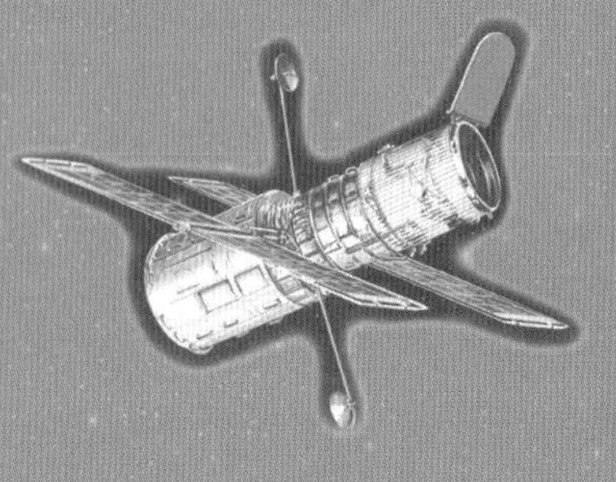

◀ Hubble telescope

The Hubble circles the Earth and takes detailed pictures. It can see farther than any other similar telescope

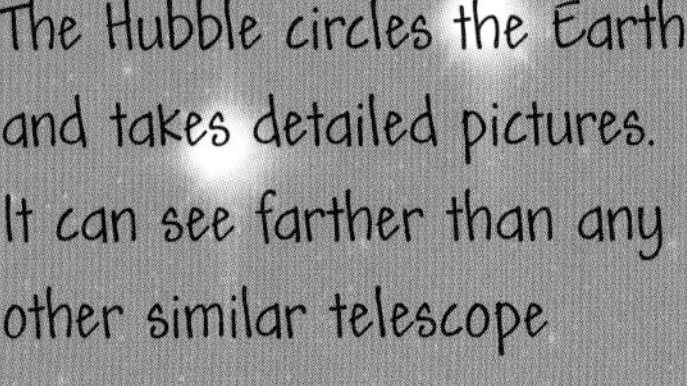

▲ The Moon

We see a full Moon when the sunlit side faces the Earth

▶ Asteroid

Asteroids are chunks of rock that travel around the Sun. There are millions of asteroids, some the size of a car, and others as big as mountains!

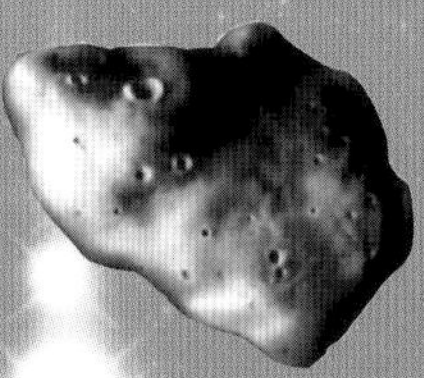

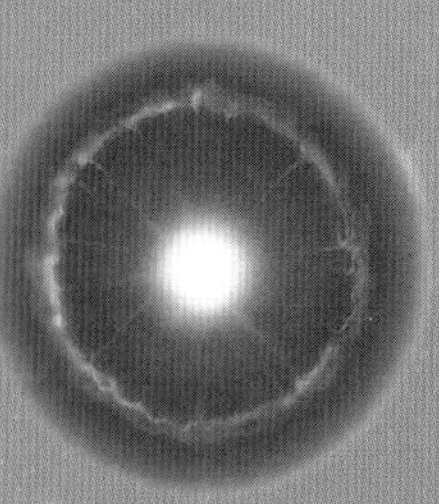

◀ New star

Stars begin their lives when they start making energy

▶ Radio telescope

These are used by astronomers to look at space to spot exciting things, such as jets of gas from black holes

KEY:

The Solar System

The Universe

Space travel

Looking into space

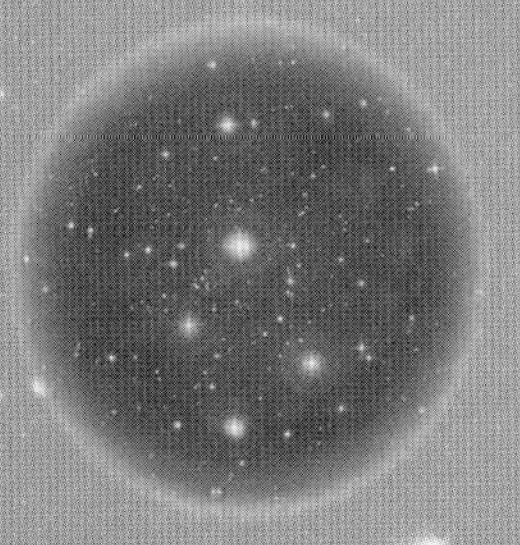

▼ Satellite telescope
These let astronomers look far into the Universe

▲ Star cluster
A star cluster has many stars of different colours and sizes, which gradually drift apart, breaking up the cluster

▲ Saturn
The shining rings around Saturn are made of millions of chunks of ice

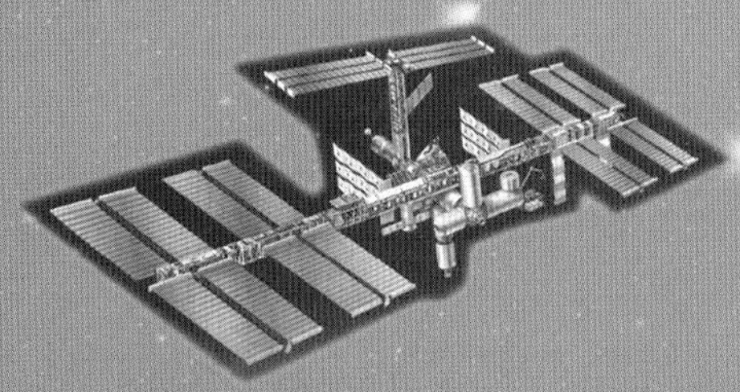

◀ International Space Station
This laboratory in space allows scientists to carry out important experiments

▲ Sojourner rover
In 1997 this robot explored Mars and gathered information about the planet

▼ Space shuttle
This spacecraft is blasted into space by three rocket engines and two huge booster rockets

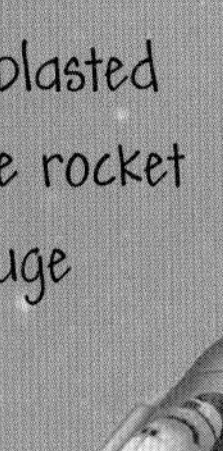

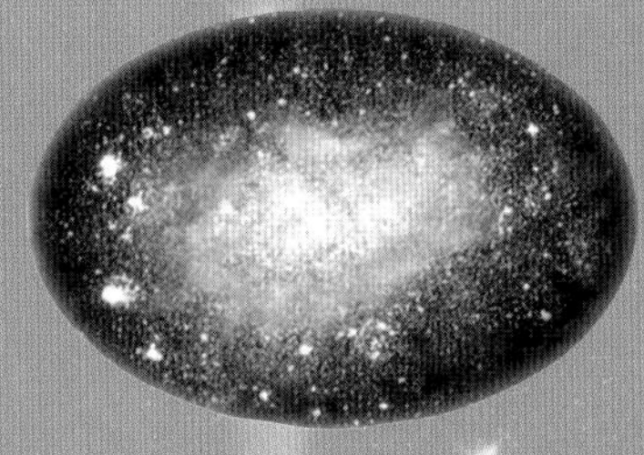

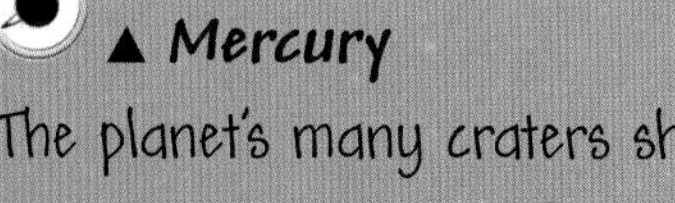

▲ Irregular galaxy
This may have formed from the leftovers of galaxies that crashed into each other

▲ Mercury
The planet's many craters show numerous space rocks have hit it

If the Sun was the size of a large beach ball, the Earth would be as small as a pea and the Moon would look like a pinhead!

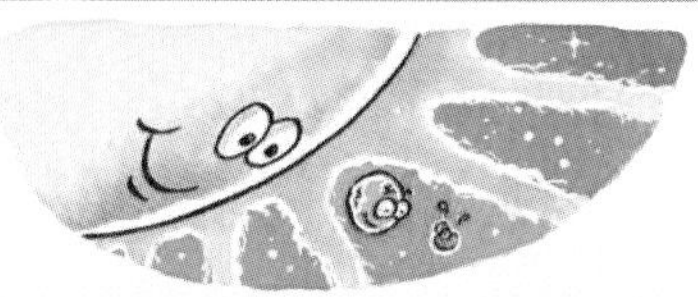

Space facts

The biggest and best!

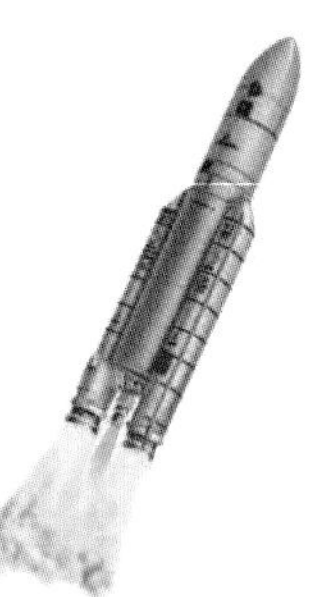

Ariane 5 is a huge rocket. It is so powerful it can launch two satellites at once.

Saturn is the lightest planet in the Solar System. If there was a large enough sea, it would float like a cork!

The Moon has no air or water. When astronauts went to the Moon they had to take air with them in their spacecraft and space suits.

Read on to find out about record-breaking planets, craters and comets

- Jupiter is the biggest planet, more massive than all the other planets in the Solar System put together! It is 11 times as wide as the Earth.

- The largest crater made by a meteorite is Meteor Crater in Arizona, USA. The hole measures 1.2 kilometres across and 175 metres deep. It was made by a meteor crashing into Earth about 50,000 years ago.

- The biggest comets are up to 180 kilometres across. The solid part of a comet is hidden inside a huge, glowing cloud that stretches into a long tail.

Q: What is an astronaut's favourite meal?

A: Launch!

What's in space?

Discover more about what is found in space

• When the Moon hides the Sun there is an eclipse. Every so often, the Sun, Moon and Earth line up in space so that the Moon comes directly between Earth and the Sun. This stops sunlight from reaching a small area on Earth.

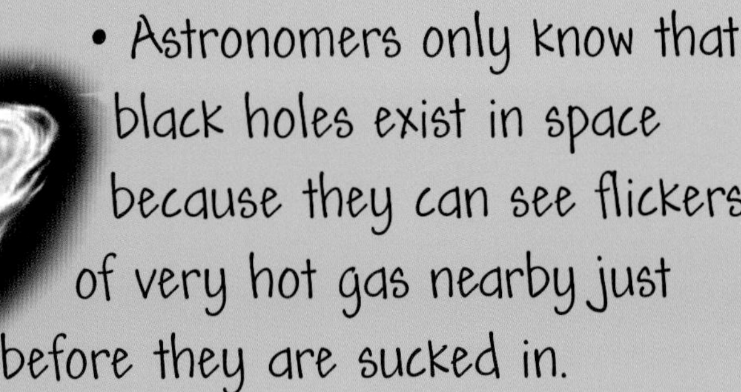

• Astronomers only know that black holes exist in space because they can see flickers of very hot gas nearby just before they are sucked in.

• Most scientists think that the Universe began with a Big Bang, about 15,000 million years ago. Since then it has been growing bigger and bigger in all directions, creating more and more space. The Universe is still expanding today.

Space facts

Millions of rocks crash into Earth as it speeds through space. Some of the larger rocks may reach the ground as meteorites.

Strong winds on Mars whip up huge dust storms that can cover the whole planet. Mars is very dry, like a desert, and is covered in red dust.

Pluto is the only planet not to have been visited by space probes.

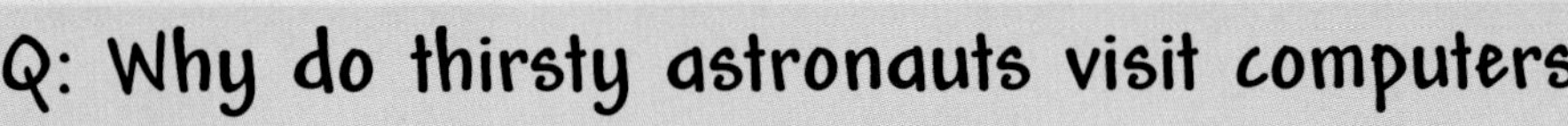

Q: Why do thirsty astronauts visit computers?

A: To use the space-bar!

Space facts

In 1969, astronauts from the US *Apollo 11* mission were the first men to land on the Moon. Neil Armstrong was the first person to set foot on the Moon.

To travel to the Sun in one of today's spacecraft would take thousands of years!

In space there is no gravity, the force that pulls things down. This means everything floats as if it has no weight.

Test your memory!

How much can you remember from your space sticker activity book? Find out below!

1. Comets are made up of which two things?
2. What is the hottest planet in the Solar System?
3. Name the only planet that has not been explored by space probes.
4. What colour is the dust on Mars?
5. Which planet has the largest volcano?
6. How many times faster than a jumbo jet does a space rocket need to blast into space?
7. Which rocket can launch two satellites at once?
8. Is Saturn, the smallest, lightest or biggest planet in the Solar System?
9. In what year did men first land on the Moon?
10. What colour are large stars?

Q: What game do spacemen like to play?
A: Astronauts and crosses!

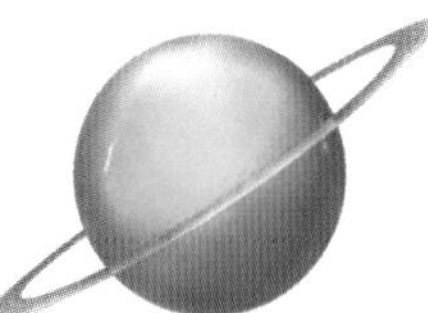

11. Does the Moon have lots of water or none at all?

12. Where is the Meteor Crater found on Earth?

13. Which planet has the most moons?

14. Name the first astronaut to walk on the Moon?

15. What type of clouds does Venus have?

16. Which is the only planet with life?

17. In what year did *Voyager 2* leave Earth?

18. What colour are Neptune's clouds?

19. Are the rings of Saturn made up of chunks of ice, lumps of rock or slithers of metal?

20. What is the family name for the Sun and its billions of stars?

Answers:

1. Dust and ice **2.** Venus **3.** Pluto **4.** Red **5.** Jupiter **6.** 40 times **7.** *Ariane 5* **8.** Lightest **9.** 1969 **10.** White **11.** None at all **12.** Arizona, USA **13.** Uranus **14.** Neil Armstrong **15.** Thick, poisonous clouds **16.** Earth **17.** 1977 **18.** Bright blue **19.** Chunks of ice **20.** The Milky Way

The Lunar rover was a moon car for astronauts to ride on. It was a small buggy with four wheels and two seats.

Hundreds of satellites circle the Earth in space. They are launched into space by rockets and may stay there for ten years or more.

Large stars are very hot and white, smaller stars are cooler and redder. Smaller stars live much longer than large stars.

Q: What do planets like to sing?

A: Nep-tunes!

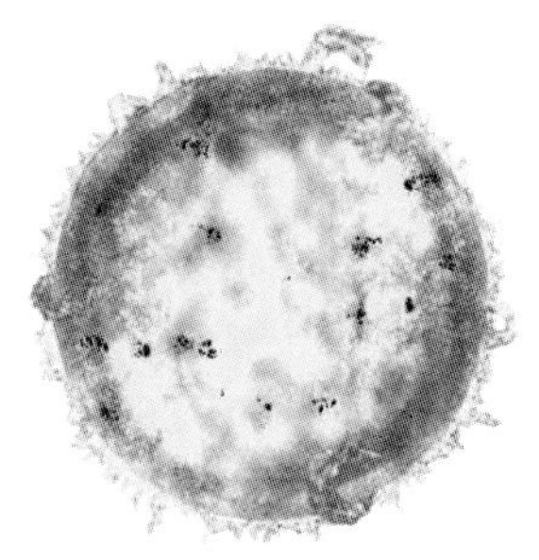

Wordsearch

EARTH

JUPITER

MARS

MERCURY

MOON

NEPTUNE

PLUTO

SATURN

SUN

URANUS

VENUS

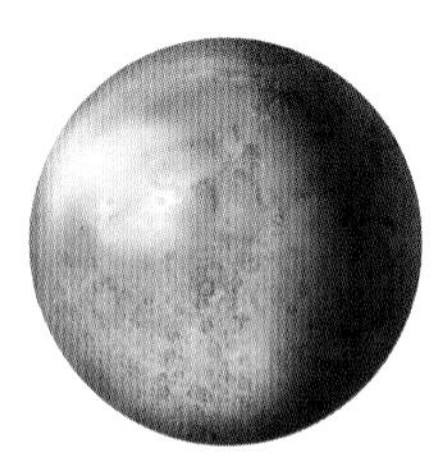

Can you find the words listed on the left, hidden in the wordsearch below?

M	A	R	S	J	K	E	Y	L	P
O	E	U	S	R	P	L	U	T	O
O	L	R	E	V	E	N	U	S	A
U	P	E	C	U	Y	V	E	I	J
R	M	P	O	U	K	E	A	L	U
A	N	O	E	A	R	T	H	G	P
N	S	E	O	S	U	Y	S	K	I
U	C	U	P	N	R	A	U	P	T
S	B	N	N	E	P	T	U	N	E
A	T	S	A	T	U	R	N	L	R

ON THE MOVE

Introduction

Planes, trains and trucks – all of these things help us travel from one place to another. Everyday we see bicycles, cars and buses taking people to work or to school, helping them to get there on time. That's what transport is all about.

Transport keeps things moving in the world of work. Huge trucks carry heavy loads, powerful tractors help farmers plough fields and by blasting off to explore space, the super-fast space shuttle helps us learn more about the Universe.

With this great sticker book you can learn about all different kinds of transport and amaze your friends with fast facts!

Mini stickers!

Is it a car, plane, train or boat? How many kinds of transport have you used or seen today? Use your mini stickers to find out about lots of different types of transport and how they are used.

Cars – family cars to record-breaking race cars

Two wheels – motorbikes, scooters and bicycles

Space – amazing vehicles used to explore space

Trains – running on tracks, a fast and convenient way to travel

Air – slow or super-fast air travel

Water – underwater or on the water

Working vehicles – vehicles to do different jobs

Cars

▲ Model T Ford

▲ Bluebird

▲ Morgan T4

▲ VW Beetle

▲ Bugatti Veyron

▲ Aston Martin DB5

Two wheels

▲ Vespa scooter

▲ Mountain bike

▲ Penny farthing

▲ Golden Flash motorbike

▲ Suzuki motorbike

Space

▲ Space shuttle

▲ Space shuttle launcher

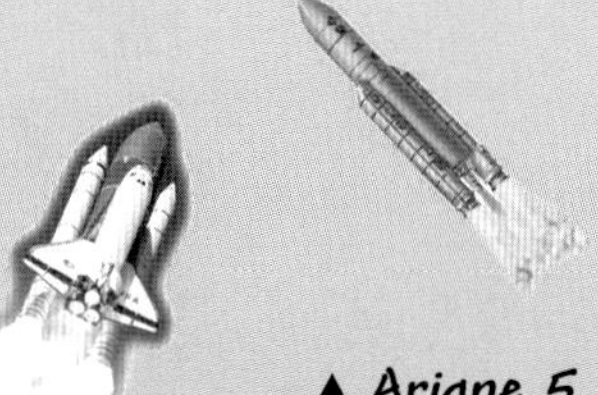

▲ Ariane 5

Trains

▶ Eurostar

▲ Early locomotive

▲ Maglev train

Air

▲ Hot-air balloon

▲ Hawk jet

▲ Helicopter

▲ Boeing 747

Water

▲ Viking longship

▲ Polaris submarine

▲ Sailing dinghy

▲ Cruise ship

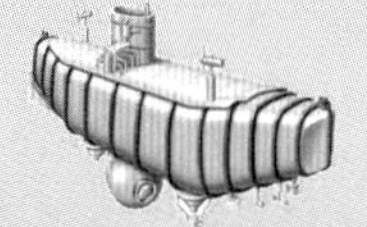

▲ Trieste submarine

Working vehicles

▲ London bus

▲ Tractor

▲ Stretch limousine

▲ Ambulance

▲ Combine harvester

▲ Articulated lorry

All kinds of transport

◀ **Space shuttle launcher**
Powerful rockets help launch the shuttle into space

▲ **Eurostar**
In 1994, this train became the first to travel from London to Paris using the Channel Tunnel

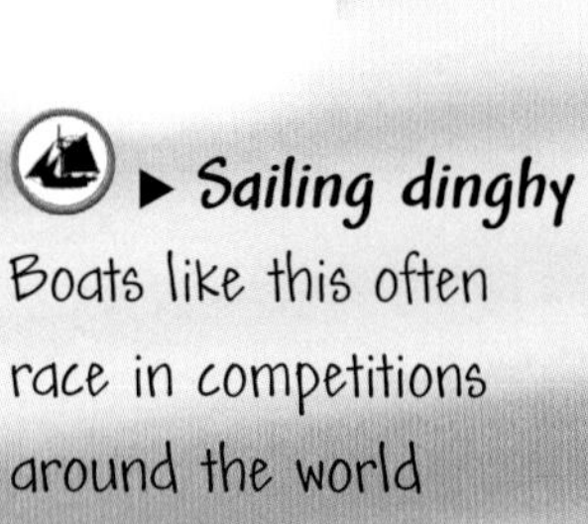

▶ **Sailing dinghy**
Boats like this often race in competitions around the world

▶ **Vespa scooter**
This classic scooter was popular during the 1960s

◀ **Morgan T4**
These vintage cars were individually assembled

▼ **Polaris submarine**
Submarines can stay underwater for months at a time

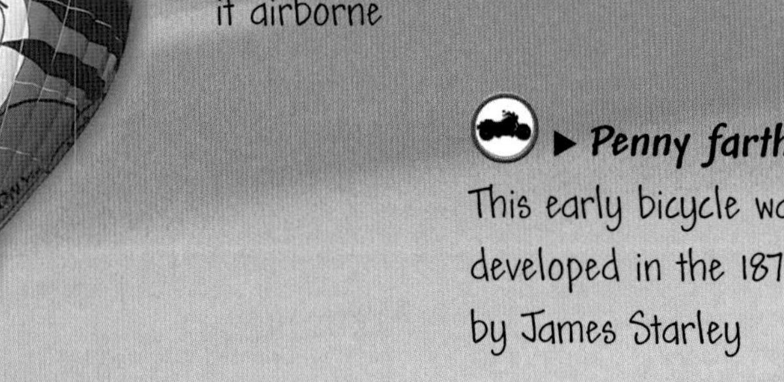

◀ **Hot-air balloon**
A burner fills the balloon with warm air to keep it airborne

▶ **Penny farthing**
This early bicycle was developed in the 1870s by James Starley

KEY:

 Cars

 Two wheels

 Space

 Trains

Air

 Water

 Working vehicles

◀ Mountain bike
These bikes have special tyres and lots of gears, and are excellent for off-road cycling

▲ Bugatti Veyron
Launched in 2003, the Veyron is a super-fast car

▼ Golden Flash motorbike
A classic motorbike first sold in 1958

▲ Maglev train
Powerful magnets suspend the train above its guide track

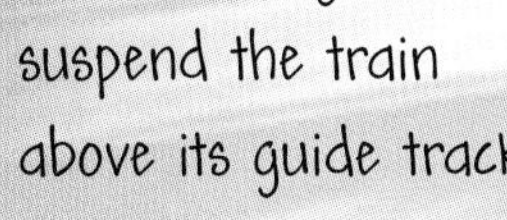

▶ Ariane 5
This huge rocket can launch two satellites at the same time

▼ Helicopter
Helicopters can fly at high speeds, hover, move sideways and land on small areas such as a rooftop

◀ Hawk jet
Aerobatics teams such as the Red Arrows use this type of jet

▶ VW Beetle
The original Beetle was first made in Germany in the 1930s

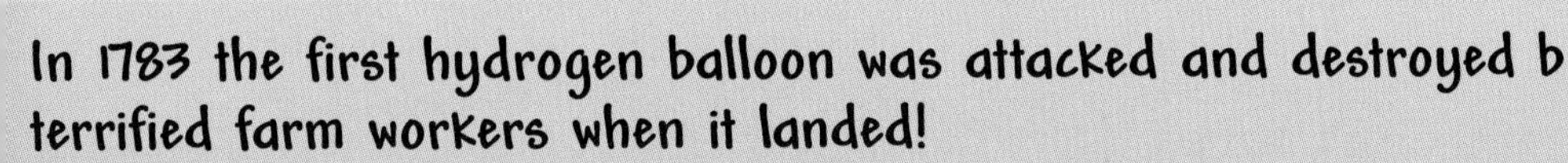

In 1783 the first hydrogen balloon was attacked and destroyed by terrified farm workers when it landed!

Building rockets

Rockets are built inside the tallest room in the world! Some space rockets are over 100 metres tall. As they are made standing upright, they need a huge building in which to be made. NASA's Vehicle Assembly Building (VAB) in Florida, United States, is 160 metres high, with massive doors that are 139 metres tall!

Space shuttles are built using four main parts. Each part is designed to help with a certain stage of the journey. The shuttle has its own engines, but also has a fuel tank and two booster rockets attached to it to help it into space.

Make a space shuttle

You will need:

• white card • scissors • plastic bottle • sticky tape • yogurt pots • silver foil • stickers • coloured paper

1. Ask an adult to help you. Cut out the wings and tail from the card. Tape these to the plastic bottle.
2. Tape two yogurt-pot engines at each side.
3. Make a cardboard nose cone and tape to the bottle.
4. Decorate your space shuttle with stickers and silver foil. Stick coloured strips of paper inside the yogurt pots for a fiery engine.

NASA moves shuttles from the VAB on crawlers – trucks that weigh 2700 tonnes each

All kinds of transport

▲ Hot-air balloon

▲ Penny farthing

▲ Eurostar

▲ Morgan T4

▲ Space shuttle launcher

▲ Sailing dinghy

▲ Vespa scooter

▲ Polaris submarine

◀ Hot-air balloon

▼ Penny farthing

▼ Morgan T4

▶ Eurostar

▶ Space shuttle launcher

◀ Sailing dinghy

▼ Vespa scooter

◀ Polaris submarine

All kinds of transport

▲ Golden Flash motorbike

▶ Maglev train

◀ Hawk jet

▲ VW Beetle

▲ Mountain bike

▶ Ariane 5

▲ Helicopter

▶ Bugatti Veyron

▲ Golden Flash motorbike

▲ Maglev train

▲ Hawk jet

▲ VW Beetle

▲ Mountain bike

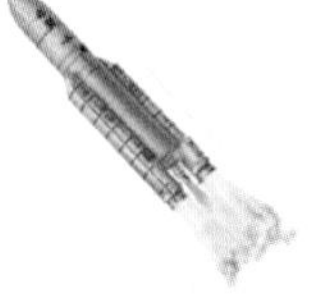

▲ Ariane 5

▲ Helicopter

▲ Bugatti Veyron

▶ Early locomotive

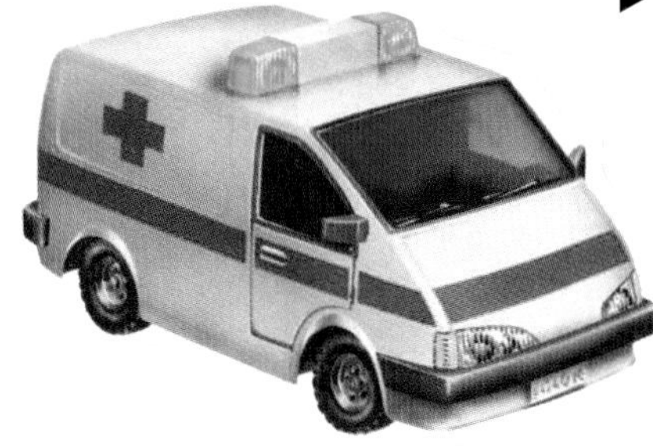

▲ Ambulance

▼ Combine harvester

▲ Space shuttle

◀ Model T Ford

▼ Bluebird

▲ Suzuki motorbike

▶ Viking longship

▲ Ambulance

▲ Early locomotive

▲ Space shuttle

▲ Combine harvester

▲ Model T Ford

▲ Suzuki motorbike

▲ Bluebird

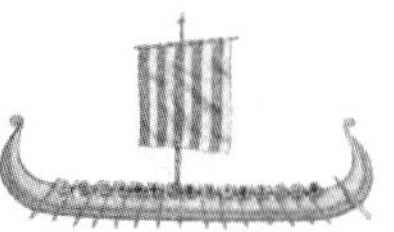

▲ Viking longship

All kinds of transport

▸ London bus

▲ Aston Martin DB5

▲ Boeing 747

▲ Tractor

▲ Articulated lorry

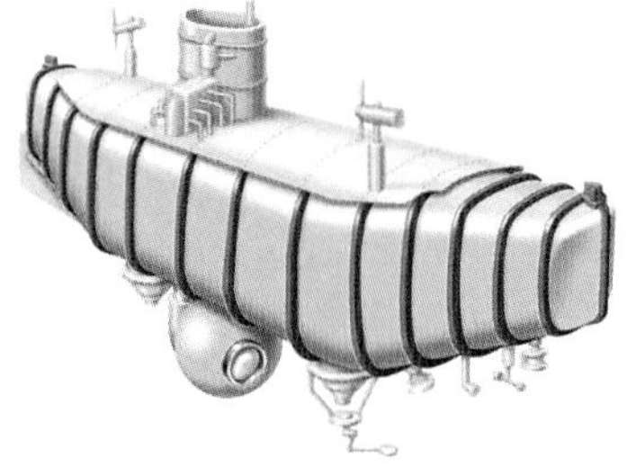

▲ Trieste submarine

▲ Cruise ship

◂ Stretch limousine

▲ Aston Martin DB5

▲ London bus

▲ Boeing 747

▲ Tractor

▲ Articulated lorry

▲ Trieste submarine

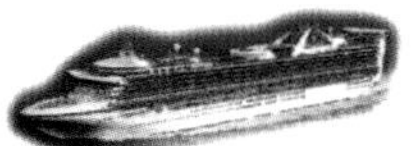

▲ Cruise ship

▲ Stretch limousine

Monster trucks

Monster trucks are normal trucks that have been customized – given massive wheels and carefully tuned engines. They are very powerful and can even drive over rows of cars!

At some motor shows, these enormous trucks race against each other. The competition course often involves driving over a range of obstacles – the fastest time wins!

The monster truck drivers are highly skilled and very brave! The trucks are brightly painted and decorated and have special monster nicknames – what would you call your monster truck?

The bars on the front of the monster truck help it push its way through any obstacles!

These wide, heavy-duty tyres are usually found on tractors. Putting these tyres on a truck gives it excellent gripping power and turns it into monster truck!

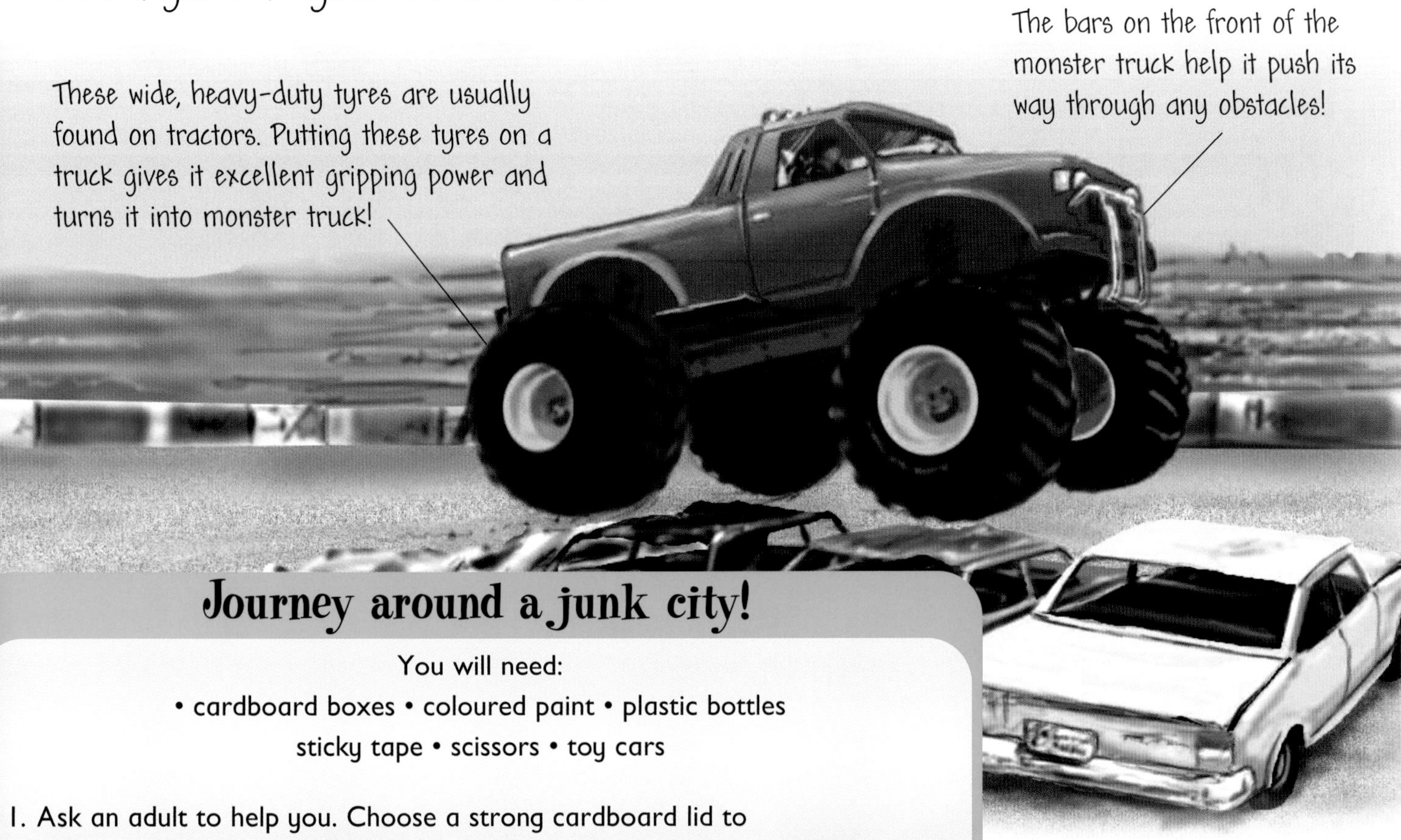

Journey around a junk city!

You will need:
• cardboard boxes • coloured paint • plastic bottles
sticky tape • scissors • toy cars

1. Ask an adult to help you. Choose a strong cardboard lid to use as a base to your city. Decide which transport features you want to include, such as roads and a train track, then paint them out on the card base.
2. Paint different sized boxes and pots for buildings and stick them to the base.
3. Push toy cars along the roads to find the best routes to travel around your junk city!

▲ During competitions monster truck drivers have to wear a strong safety harness, crash helmet and full protective clothing to keep them safe in the truck.

All kinds of transport

▶ Suzuki motorbike
Popular road motorbikes are often based on race models

▲ Bluebird
In 1931 Bluebird, driven by Sir Malcolm Campbell, took the land-speed record

▼ Early locomotive
Burning coal in its firebox produced steam to power the locomotive

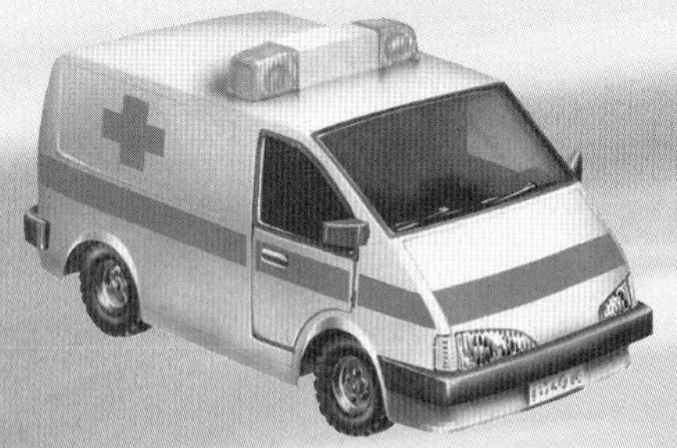

▲ Space shuttle
In 1981, the first shuttle mission lasted two days and covered 1.73 million kilometres

▲ Ambulance
Ambulances are fully-equipped to offer emergency medical care

▼ Combine harvester
Most modern combine harvesters have air-conditioned, soundproofed cabs

▲ Viking longship
Viking warriors used these long, narrow boats

▲ Model T Ford
Tough, cheap and reliable, this was the first mass-produced car

Cars

Two wheels

Space

Trains

Air

Water

Working vehicles

▶ Articulated lorry

Large articulated lorries are used to transport goods across the world

▲ Boeing 747

You can fly non-stop for 10,000 kilometres in a Boeing 747

▼ Trieste submarine

In 1960, Trieste took the record for the deepest dive – over 10,915 metres

▼ Cruise ship

Large cruise ships offer relaxing holidays with excellent facilities

▼ Stretch limousine

Extravagant limousine cars are often used by the rich and famous to travel around in

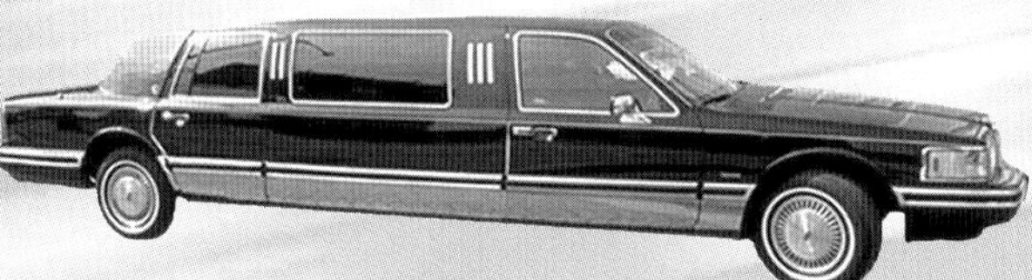

▼ London bus

First introduced in 1956, these buses are still in service today

▶ Tractor

Huge wheels help prevent the tractor from sinking into the ground

◀ Aston Martin DB5

This car is famous as James Bond's car in the film *Goldfinger*

Astronaut John Glenn was 77 years old when he went into space in 1998. He first travelled to space in 1962, 36 years earlier!

Fast facts

A modern racing car has thousands of parts made from hundreds of different materials! Each is suited to certain conditions such as stress, temperature and vibrations.

The first aircraft flight lasted 12 seconds. The *Flyer* travelled 37 metres and landed safely!

The first motorbike was steam-powered. It was built by the Michaux brothers in 1868.

The biggest and best!

Read on to find out about some amazing record-breaking vehicles

- The world's fastest combat jet is the Russian MiG-25. It has been tracked by radar flying at over 3300 kilometres an hour!

- The world's longest car is a 26-wheeled limousine. It is 30.5 metres long and includes a swimming pool, complete with diving board!

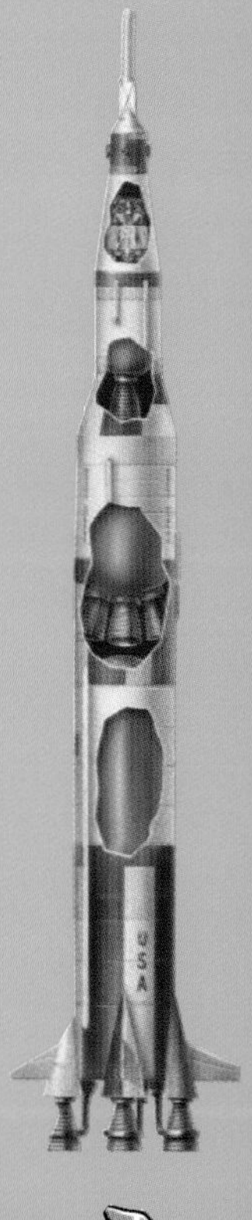

- *Saturn V* launched the Apollo mission to the Moon. It is the largest, most powerful rocket launcher ever built.

Q: When does a cart come before a horse?

A: In a dictionary!

Time to travel

Discover more interesting facts about travel and transport

• Thrust SSC, driven by Andy Green, broke the land-speed record in October 1997. It reached a top speed of 1227.99 kilometres an hour!

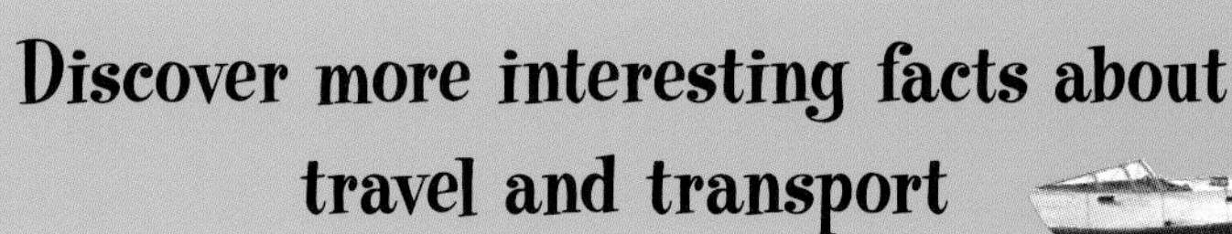

• Some cars are powered by the Sun! Cars are being developed using solar panels to charge batteries, which supply power to the car. This provides a very environmentally-friendly method of transport.

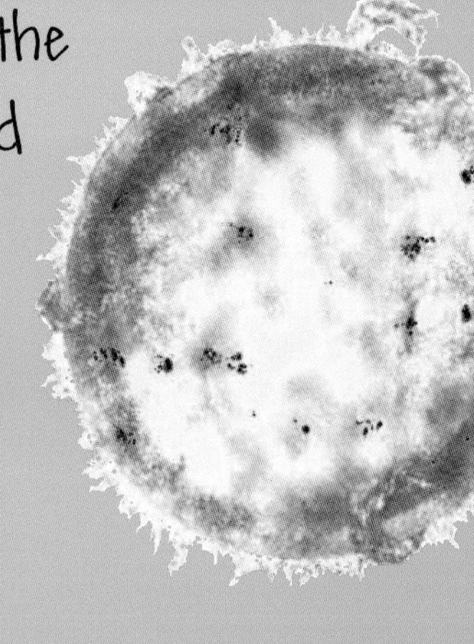

• The world's first airport was built at Croydon near London in 1928. Today, the busiest airport in the world is Hartsfield International Airport in Atlanta, USA.

Fast facts

The famous Montgolfier hot-air balloon made the first untethered manned flight in 1783.

Trams are buses that run on rails laid through city streets. They are called streetcars in the United States.

The New York City subway is the most extensive underground rail system in the world. It includes 468 stations and the trains operate 24 hours a day, seven days a week.

Q: What only starts to work when it is fired?
A: A rocket!

Fast facts

Bicycles are one of the oldest forms of transport. Today there are about one billion bicycles in the world!

A double-decker bus can carry the same number of people as 20 cars!

The biggest and strongest locomotives ever were nicknamed 'Big Boy'. They could haul massive freight trains over the Rocky Mountains.

Test your memory!

How much can you remember from your transport sticker activity book? Find out below!

1. Which rocket launched the Apollo mission to the Moon?
2. How long did the first aircraft flight last?
3. In what year did astronaut John Glenn first travel into space?
4. What are trams called in the United States?
5. The Russian MiG-25 has been tracked by radar flying at how many kilometres an hour?
6. James Bond drove which car in the film *Goldfinger*?
7. Which train travels from London to Paris through the Channel Tunnel?
8. In which city is NASA's Vehicle Assembly Building?
9. How is the Maglev train suspended?
10. Where was the world's first airport built?

Q: What type of ship lies shaking on the seabed?

A: A nervous wreck!

11. Do monster trucks have lightweight, narrow tyres or heavy-duty, wide tyres?
12. Who drove the *Bluebird* to take the land-speed record in 1931?
13. What powered the first motorbike?
14. How many stations does the subway in New York City have?
15. What was the first mass-produced car?
16. The *Trieste* submarine took which record in 1960?
17. How long is the world's longest car?
18. James Starley developed which bicycle in the 1870s?
19. In which country was the VW Beetle first made?
20. Is the world's busiest airport in Atlanta, London or New York?

Answers:
1. Saturn V **2.** 12 seconds **3.** 1962 **4.** Streetcars
5. 3300 **6.** Aston Martin DB5 **7.** Eurostar
8. Florida **9.** By powerful magnets **10.** Croydon, UK
11. Large, heavy-duty tyres **12.** Sir Malcolm Campbell
13. Steam **14.** 468 **15.** Model T Ford **16.** The deepest dive
17. 30.5 metres **18.** Penny farthing
19. Germany **20.** Atlanta

Q: When is a car not a car?
A: When it turns into a garage!

Fast facts

The Trans-Siberian Express makes the world's longest train journey at over 9438 kilometres.

The fastest helicopter is the Westland Lynx, which flew at 402 kilometres an hour on 6 August 1986.

In 1522, Ferdinand Magellan's ship *Victoria* made the first round-the-world voyage.

Wordsearch

Can you find the words listed on the left, hidden in the wordsearch below?

BUS

CAR

HELICOPTER

JET

LORRY

MOTORBIKE

SCOOTER

SHUTTLE

SUBMARINE

TRACTOR

TRAIN

H	E	L	I	C	O	P	T	E	R
S	O	A	L	G	A	B	U	P	I
U	S	M	F	J	T	R	A	I	N
B	C	H	L	E	U	L	H	H	T
M	O	T	O	R	B	I	K	E	R
A	O	S	R	O	O	U	H	L	A
R	T	T	R	A	J	K	S	I	C
I	E	A	Y	R	T	E	L	C	T
N	R	C	A	B	H	R	T	D	O
E	D	S	H	U	T	T	L	E	R

SHARKS

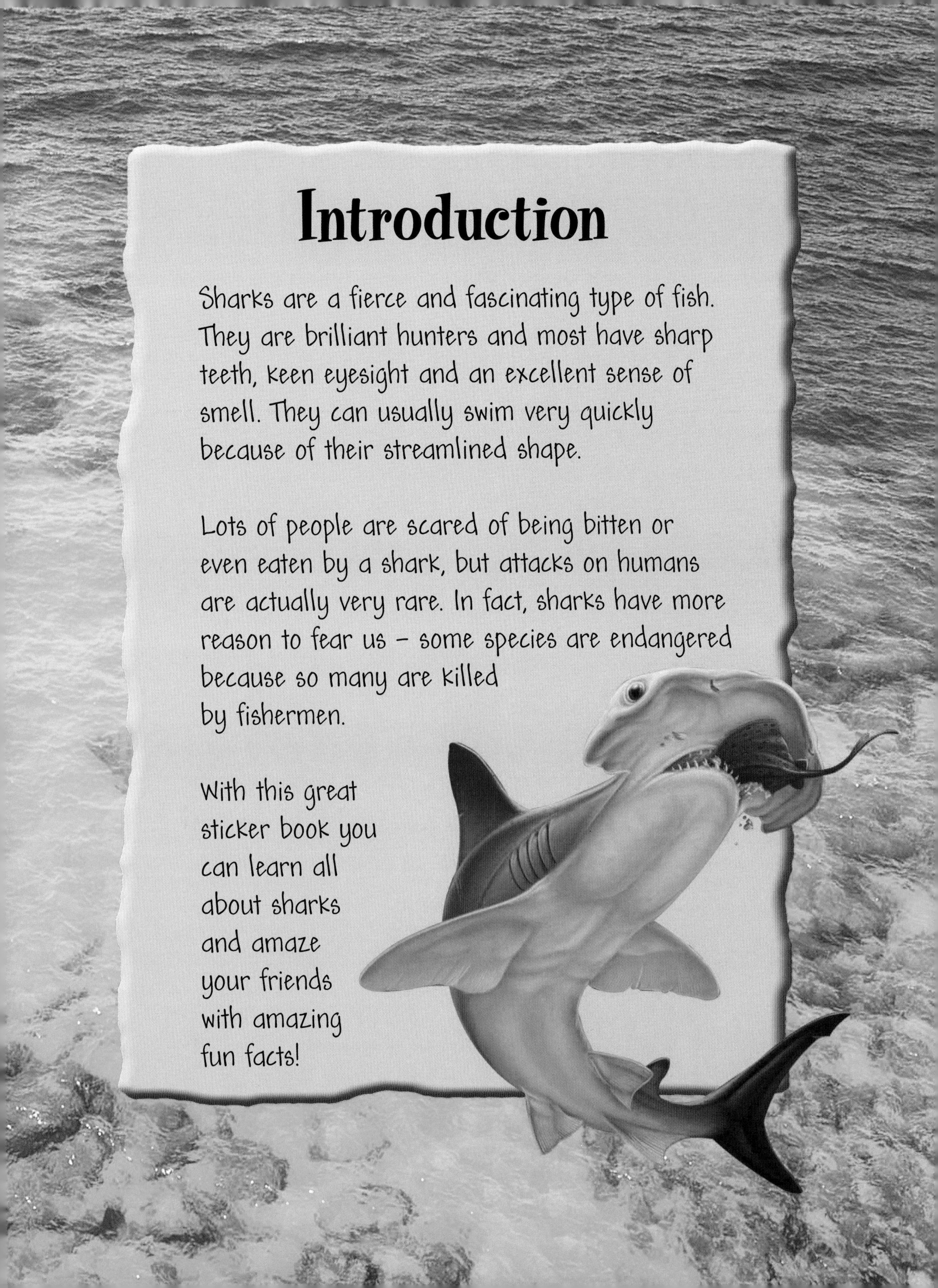

Introduction

Sharks are a fierce and fascinating type of fish. They are brilliant hunters and most have sharp teeth, keen eyesight and an excellent sense of smell. They can usually swim very quickly because of their streamlined shape.

Lots of people are scared of being bitten or even eaten by a shark, but attacks on humans are actually very rare. In fact, sharks have more reason to fear us – some species are endangered because so many are killed by fishermen.

With this great sticker book you can learn all about sharks and amaze your friends with amazing fun facts!

Mini stickers!

What is a filter feeder? How long can the whale shark grow? Which shark has spikes all over its body? Use your mini stickers to find out about the lives of extraordinary and fierce sharks and their relatives.

Extraordinary sharks – weird and wonderful sharks
How sharks live – how and where sharks live
Shark relatives – these are closely related to sharks
Fierce sharks – the biggest and scariest members of the shark family

Extraordinary sharks

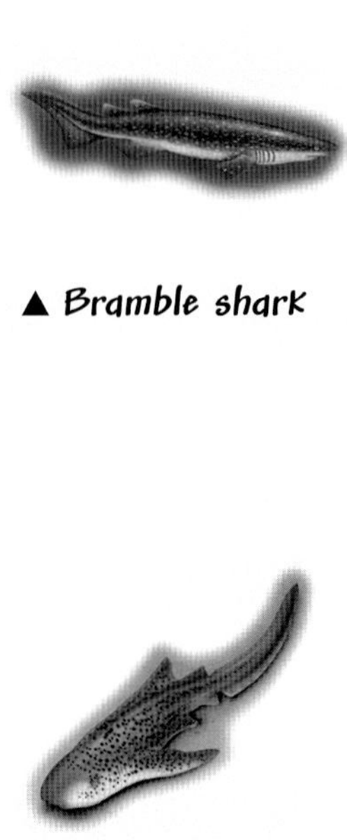

▲ Bramble shark

▼ Megamouth shark

▲ Lanternshark

▲ Weasel shark

▲ Zebra shark

▲ Thresher shark

▲ Whale shark

◀ Crocodile shark

▲ Dogfish shark

▲ Frilled shark

▼ Port Jackson shark

▲ Black-tip reef shark

How sharks live

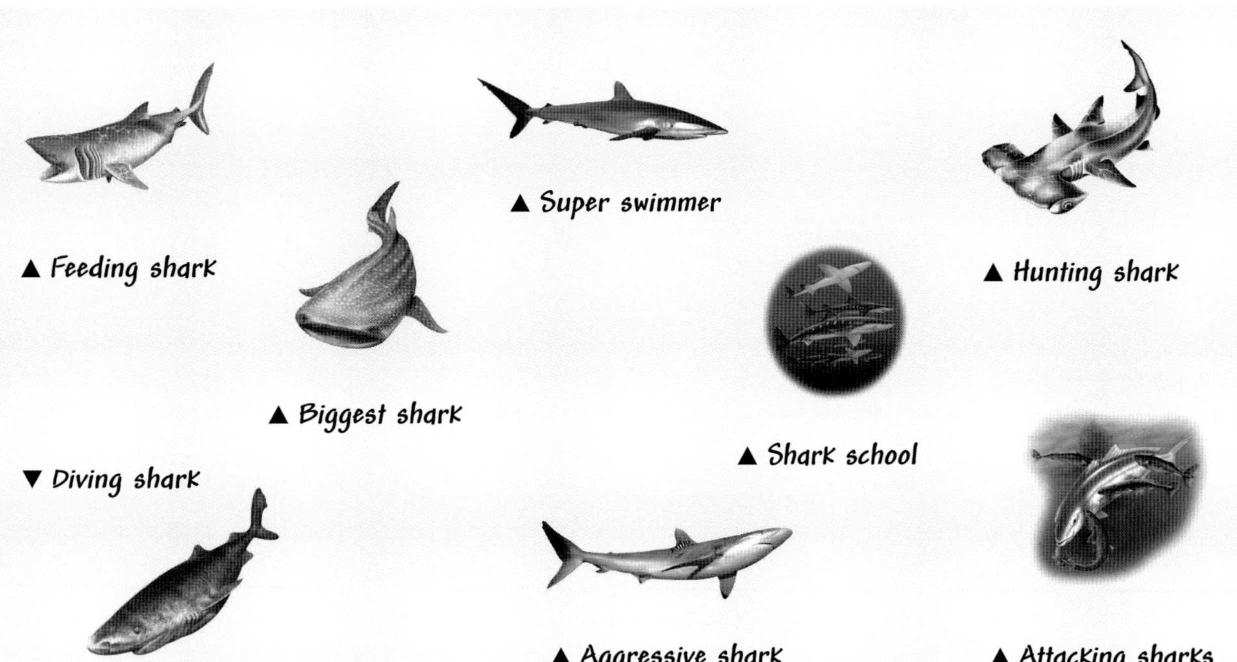

Shark relatives

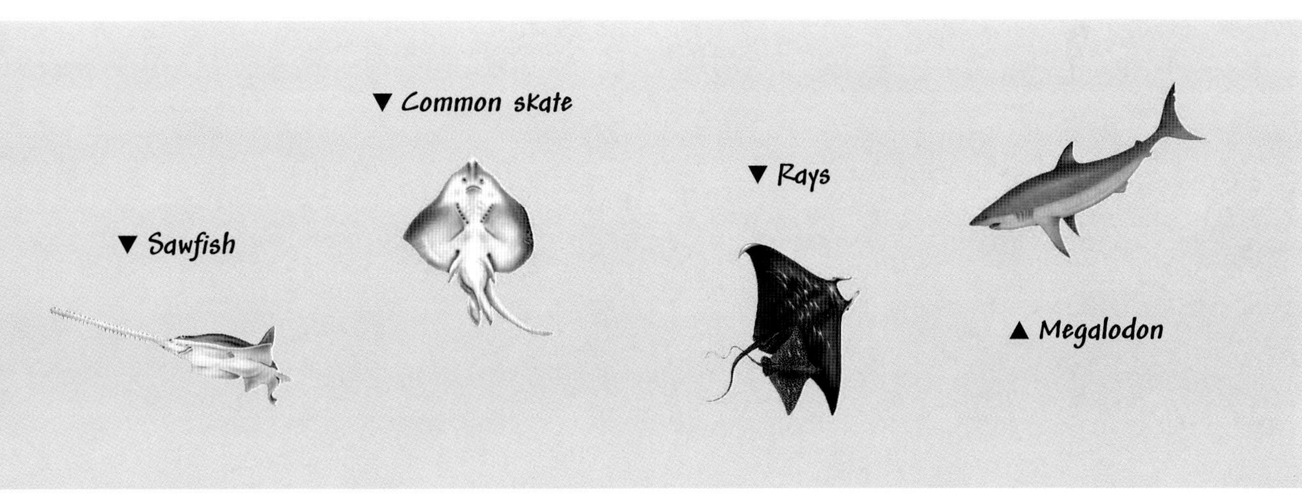

Fierce sharks

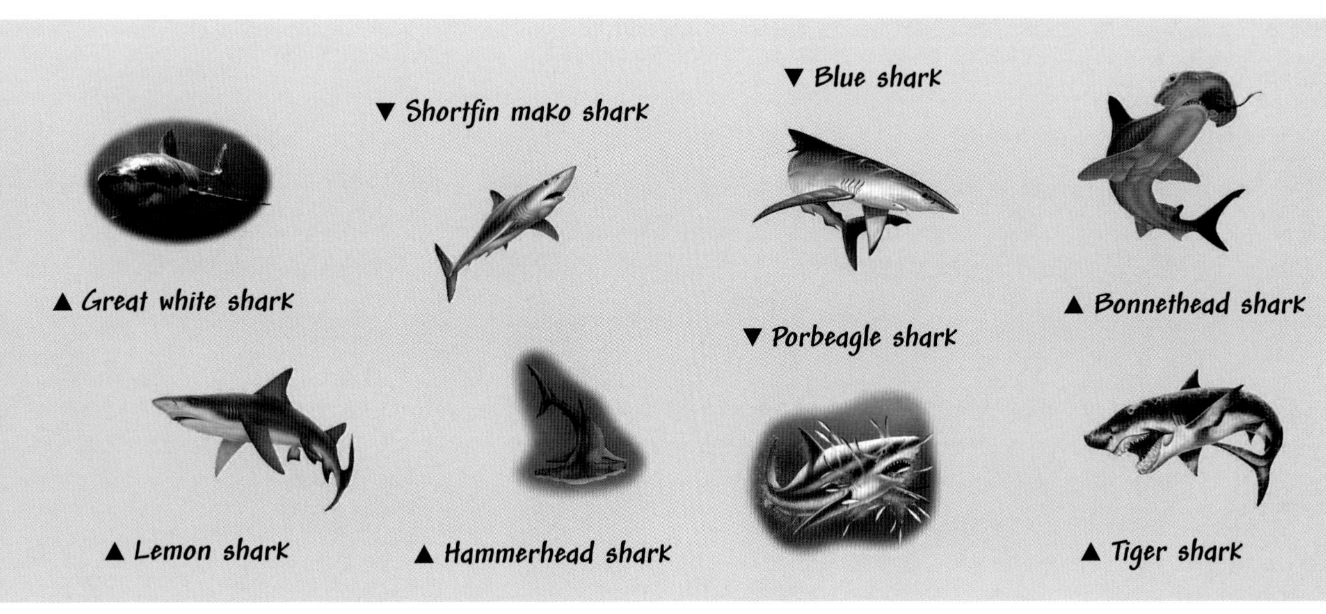

All kinds of sharks

◀ Bonnethead shark
Fishermen have to be careful if they grab a bonnethead by the tail, as it can reach up and bite their hand

◀ Frilled shark
This shark is often mistaken for an eel or a sea snake because of its snakelike appearance

▼ Bramble shark
A shark that lives in deep water and has large, thornlike spikes all over its body

▼ Lanternshark
Glowing lights on their bodies give these sharks their name

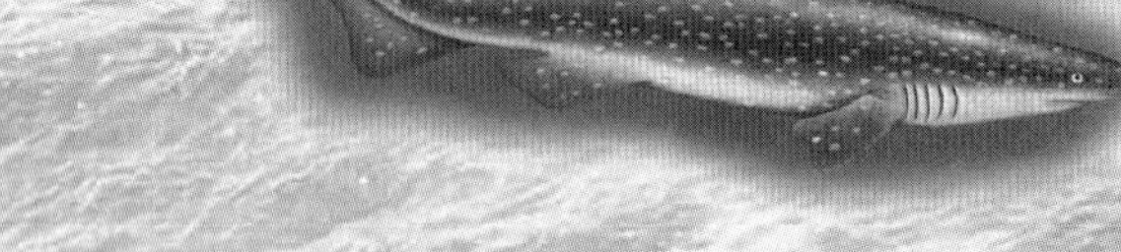

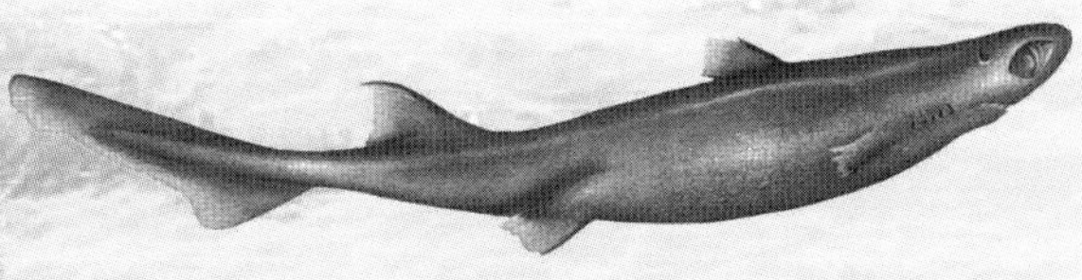

▼ Feeding shark
This basking shark feeds on tiny creatures that live in the water

▶ Biggest shark
Whale sharks are the biggest sharks and they use their massive mouths to sieve food out of the water

▶ Megamouth shark
This shark lives up to its name with a mouth about one metre in width!

▲ Sawfish
A sawfish is a type of ray and it gets its name from its long sawlike snout

KEY:

How sharks live

Extraordinary sharks

Shark relatives

Fierce sharks

▼ Crocodile shark
The huge eyes of this shark take up almost half its head!

▲ Super swimmer
Sharks are streamlined so that they can swim quickly and sneak up on their prey

▶ Pygmy sharks
Some sharks work as a group to attack bigger fish that are sick or injured

◀ Hunting shark
At night, bonnetheads go hunting alone for fish, squid, octopuses, crabs and stingrays

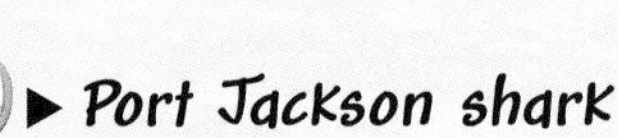

▶ Port Jackson shark
After laying her eggs, the female Port Jackson shark picks up her egg cases in her mouth and wedges them in a safe place

▶ Common skate
Skates are like rays and mostly live in deep water – as far as 3000 metres down

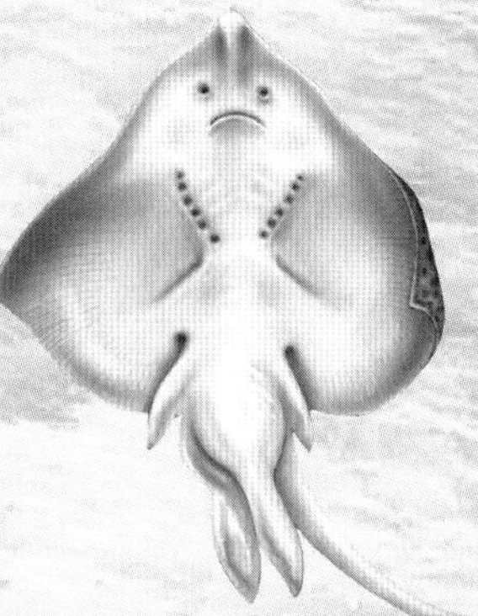

◀ Diving shark
Most sharks like shallow or warm seas, but Greenland sharks dive deep in the cold water of the North Atlantic Ocean

◀ Weasel shark
This shark looks like a bite has been taken out of its tail – but this is just its natural shape

A typical shark has several hundred teeth at any one time!

Scales and skin!

A shark's skin is covered by small scales. These are very sharp and pointed – in fact, they are just like tiny teeth. The saw shark also has teeth outside its mouth. These run in a row along each side of its long snout.

The saw shark 'saws' into mud and seaweed to find fish and starfish, and eats them using the teeth in its mouth.

Make a saw shark mask!

You will need:

• scissors • cardboard • pen • string

1. Draw the shape of a saw shark's zig-zig nose and head.
2. Carefully cut out the shark shape.
3. Draw on the shark's eyes.
4. Ask an adult to make two holes in the top of the mask and thread the string through to finish your shark mask.

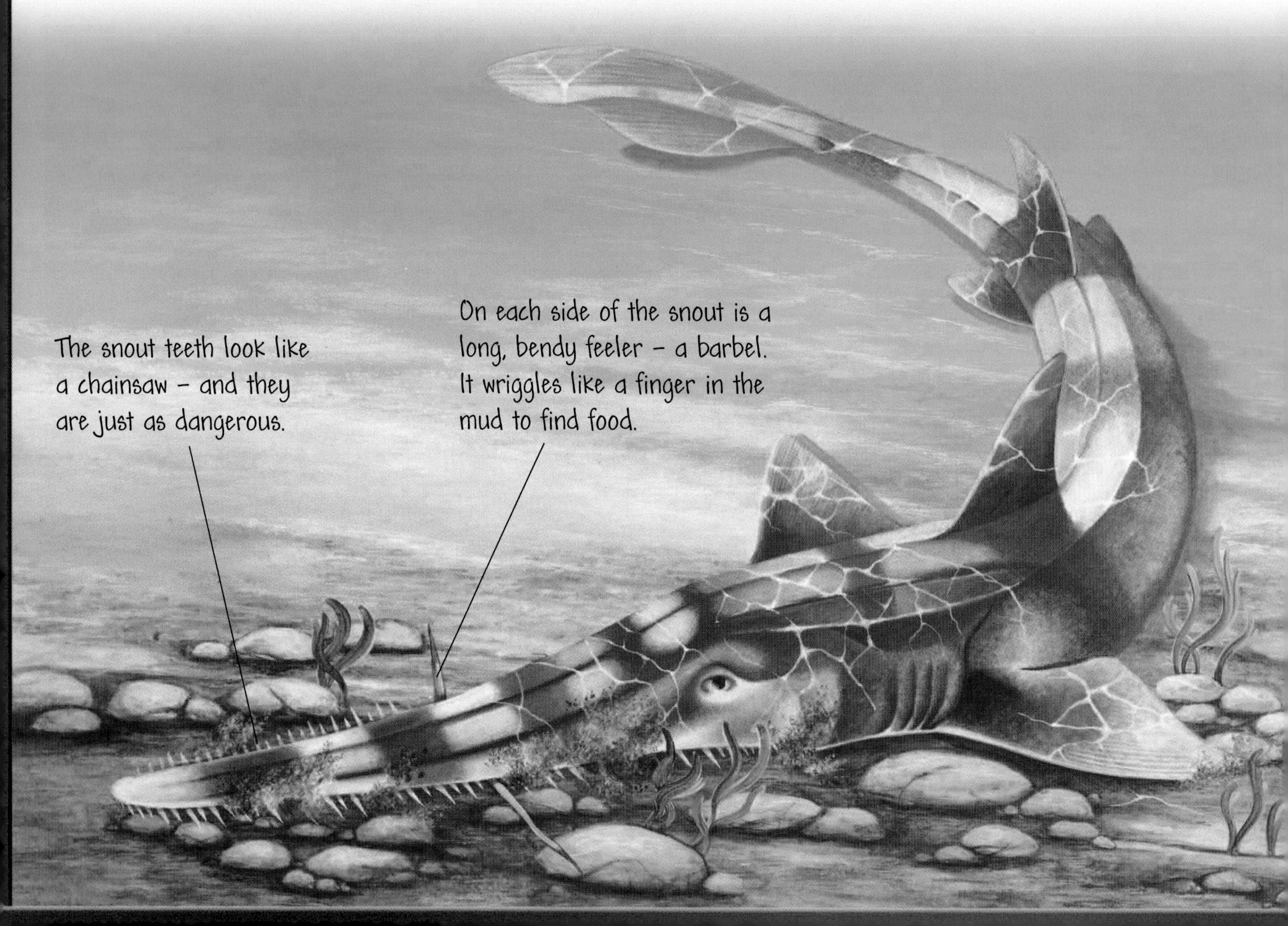

The snout teeth look like a chainsaw – and they are just as dangerous.

On each side of the snout is a long, bendy feeler – a barbel. It wriggles like a finger in the mud to find food.

All kinds of sharks

▲ Bramble shark

▲ Sawfish

▲ Megamouth shark

▲ Bonnethead shark

▲ Feeding shark

▲ Biggest shark

▲ Frilled shark

▲ Lanternshark

▼ Bramble shark

▲ Sawfish

▲ Megamouth shark

▼ Bonnethead shark

► Feeding shark

◄ Biggest shark

▲ Frilled shark

▼ Lanternshark

All kinds of sharks

▲ Super swimmer

▲ Weasel shark

▲ Diving shark

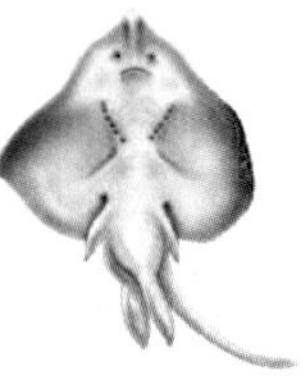

▲ Common skate

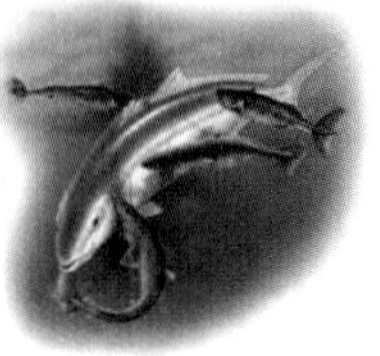

▲ Attacking sharks

▲ Port Jackson shark

▲ Crocodile shark

▲ Hunting shark

▼ Super swimmer

▲ Weasel shark

▶ Diving shark

▶ Common skate

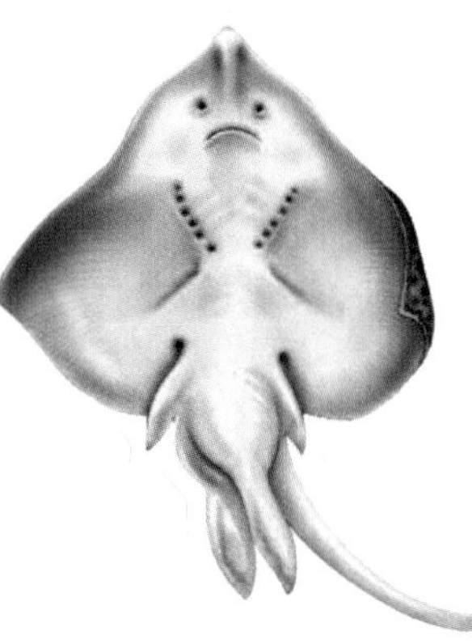

▲ Attacking sharks

▼ Port Jackson shark

▼ Crocodile shark

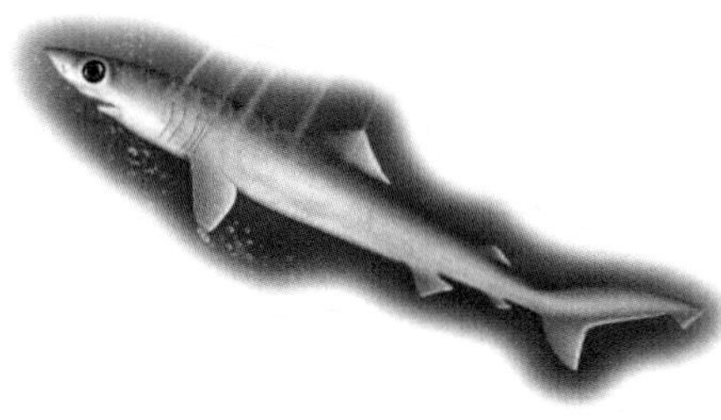

▶ Hunting shark

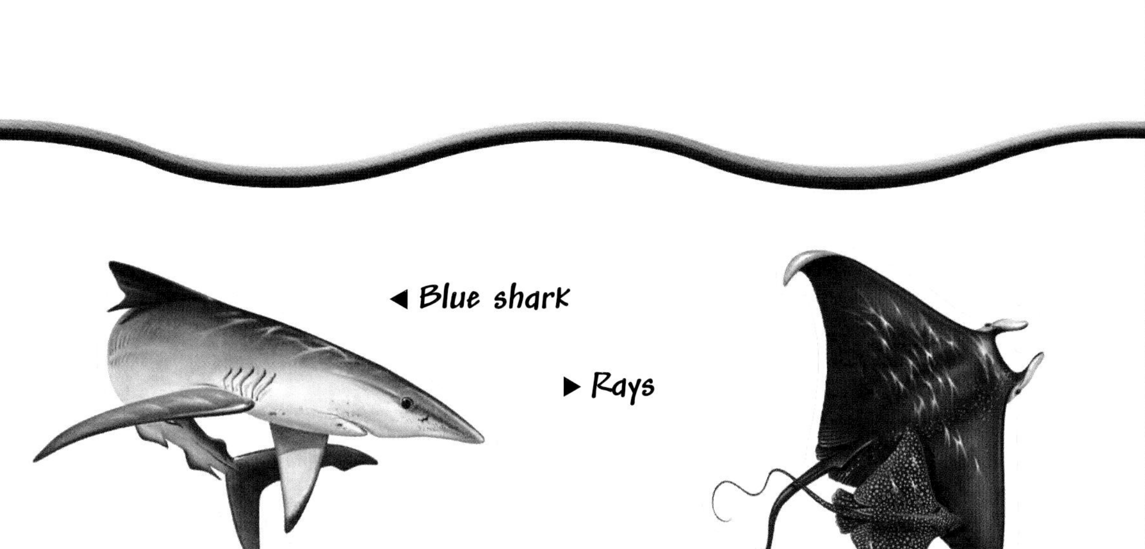

◀ Blue shark

▶ Rays

▼ Thresher shark

▲ Black-tip reef shark

▶ Shark school

▲ Hammerhead shark

▼ Shortfin mako shark

▲ Great white shark

▲ Blue shark

▲ Rays

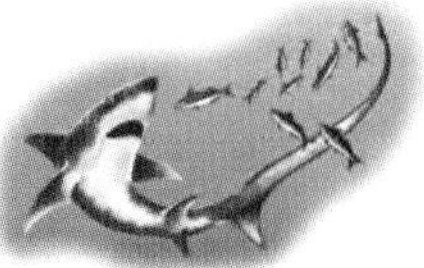

▲ Thresher shark

▲ Black-tip reef shark

▲ Shark school

▲ Hammerhead shark

▲ Shortfin Mako

▲ Great white shark

All kinds of sharks

▼ Whale shark

▲ Megalodon

▼ Dogfish shark

▼ Porbeagle shark

▼ Tiger shark

▼ Zebra shark

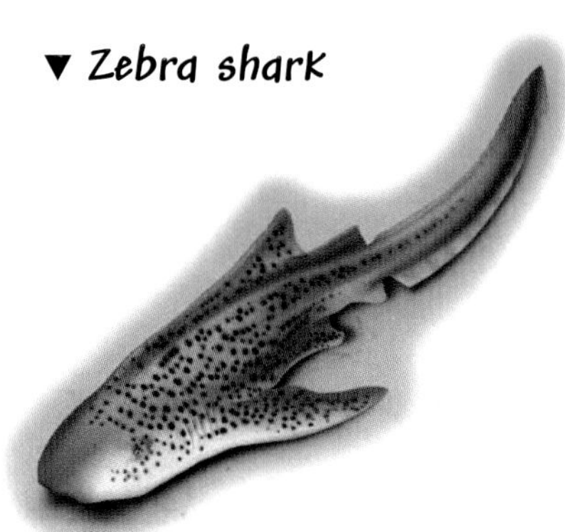

▼ Aggressive shark

▲ Lemon shark

▲ Megalodon

▲ Whale shark

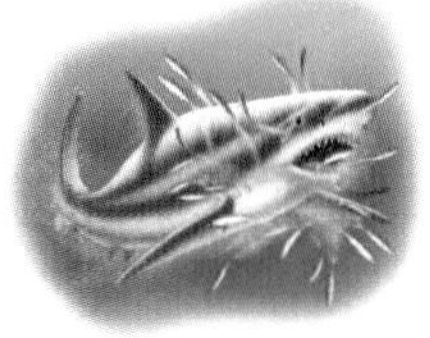

▲ Porbeagle shark

▲ Dogfish shark

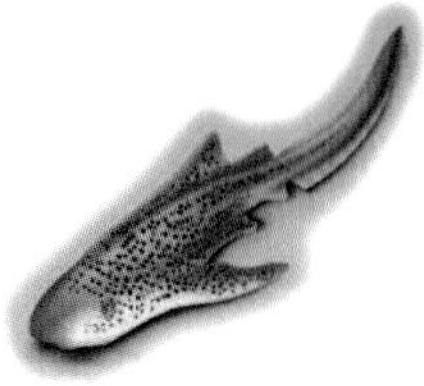

▲ Zebra shark

▲ Tiger shark

▲ Aggressive shark

▲ Lemon shark

Giant shark!

Most sharks are big. The whale shark is a giant – it grows to more than 15 metres long and can weigh over 20 tonnes! It is the world's biggest fish, but is not a fierce hunter.

A whale shark swims with its mouth open, filtering small animals such as fish and krill from the water with its special comblike gills. Like all sharks, it cannot chew – it just swallows its food whole!

Shark race for two!

You will need:

• tissue paper • scissors • newspapers • plates

1. Cut out two tissue-paper sharks. Each one should be about 30 centimetres long.
2. Lie the sharks flat on their backs. Place two plates about 3 metres away on the other side of the room.
3. Hit the ground just behind the shark with a rolled-up newspaper to make it move. The shark that lands on the plate first is the winner.

Shark time

 **Rays**

Filter feeders, like the basking and whale shark – rays suck in seawater and filter tiny plankton out of it

▶ **Great white shark**

Fish, seals and sealions are the favourite foods of great whites

▶ **Hammerhead shark**

These are some of the smartest sharks – they are fast, fierce hunters

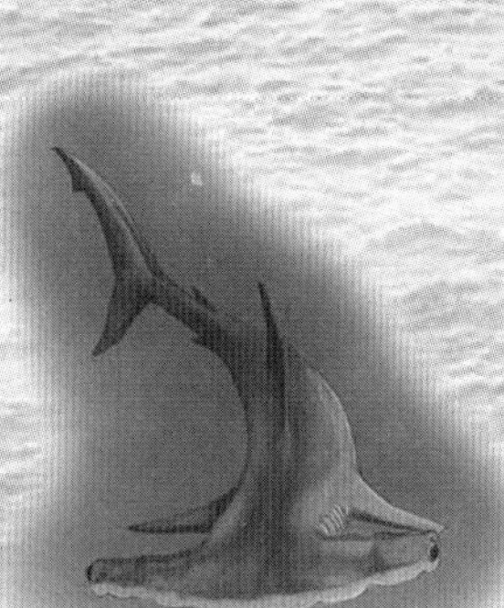

▶ **Shortfin mako shark**

Recorded swimming at over 30 kilometres per hour, this is the fastest shark

▼ **Thresher shark**

The thresher shark sweeps its enormous tail from side to side to stun small fish before eating them

◀ **Shark school**

Sharks sometimes swim in schools of hundreds or even thousands

▶ **Blue shark**

This shark does not normally attack humans, but it has been reported to attack the survivors of sunken ships

▲ **Black-tip reef shark**

These sharks have black marks on the tips of each of their fins

KEY:

 How sharks live

 Extraordinary sharks

 Shark relatives

 Fierce sharks

▶ Zebra shark

When young, zebra sharks have dark and light stripes – as adults the stripes separate into blotches

▶ Megalodon

Probably the biggest shark ever, Megalodon lived millions of years ago – it may have been very similar to a great white shark

▼ Aggressive shark

An upward-pointed snout, arched back and downward-pointed fins means this shark is in a bad mood and ready to attack

▼ Whale shark

The largest shark in the world, the whale shark can be up to 12 metres long!

▶ Porbeagle shark

The porbeagle can travel long distances, following schools of fish around the ocean

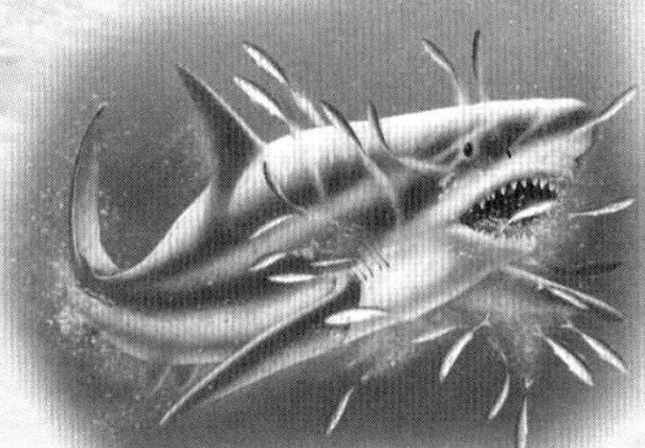

▼ Lemon shark

Stings from stingrays have been found embedded in the mouths of lemon sharks

▲ Tiger shark

Tiger sharks have even been seen eating other tiger sharks!

▶ Dogfish shark

There are around 80 shark species that make up the huge dogfish family

A reindeer was once found inside a dead Greenland shark's stomach!

Fun facts

Biggest and best

Mako sharks can leap 6 metres clear of the water's surface.

There is a better chance of winning the lottery than being attacked by a shark.

In 1758 it was reported that a sailor had been swallowed whole by a shark, it is said that the shark was made to throw up and the man was recovered unharmed!

Read more about some record-breaking sharks

- The longest shark in the sea is the whale shark – it can grow up to 15 metres long. That is more than four times bigger than the average human!

- Megalodon lived over 2 million years ago. Scientists believe that its mouth was over 2 metres wide. That's big enough to eat several people in one go!

- The largest great white shark ever caught weighed a staggering 4.5 tonnes - that is only just lighter than a fully grown elephant!

Q: What do you get from a fierce shark?

A: As far away as possible!

Shark facts

Discover some fascinating facts about sharks

• A shark can have as many as 300 teeth at one time. If a tooth is damaged, it is quickly replaced with a new one. In a lifetime sharks can use about 20,000 teeth!

• Baby sharks are called pups. They can look after themselves as soon as they are born. Sometimes they have a small yolk sac that supplies nutrients until the young shark starts to eat properly.

• Sharks' skeletons are not made of bone, but of a material called cartilage, which is like rubber. This means that sharks are very flexible and they can twist and turn easily in the water.

Fun facts

Some shark scientists believe that spiny dogfish can live for up to 100 years!

A lemon shark has been recorded swimming at 32 kilometres per hour. The shortfin mako is thought to swim even faster.

When a shark is turned onto its back it goes limp and sleepy. This helps scientists to study them.

Q: What is yellow and dangerous?

A: Shark-infested custard!

Fun facts

Test your memory!

Sharks do not chew their food, they swallow chunks whole!

Great white sharks can go for 3 whole months without eating.

Sharks will often take a bite of something to see if they like the taste. If they don't, they spit it back out!

How much can you remember from your sharks sticker activity book? Find out below!

1. How many species are in the dogfish family: 80, 800 or 8000?
2. Which is the biggest shark ever: the megamouth, Megalodon or the mako shark?
3. Does the zebra shark have stripes when it is young?
4. What do saw sharks use their saws for?
5. Which is the fastest shark?
6. Sharks are fish: true or false?
7. What will happen to a shark if it stops swimming: will it change colour, sink or float?
8. Do sharks usually go hunting during the day or the night?
9. Where do black-tip reef sharks have their black markings?
10. How many years do some scientists believe a dogfish can live: 30, 70 or 100?

Q: What is a shark's favourite game?

A: Swallow the leader!

11. What can sharks not do: chew their food, swim or smell?

12. All sharks are blind: true or false?

13. Which of the following does the great white shark not like to eat: fish, vegetables or seals?

14. How wide is the megamouth's mouth?

15. Do sharks have fur, scales or feathers?

16. Where do Greenland sharks live?

17. What other animals are frilled sharks often mistaken for?

18. The crocodile shark has eyes that take up almost half of its head: true or false?

19. How many teeth can sharks have at once?

20. Does the Port Jackson shark give birth to live young?

Answers:

1. 80 **2.** Megalodon **3.** No – spots **4.** Digging up prey from the seabed **5.** Shortfin mako **6.** True **7.** Sink **8.** The night **9.** On the tips of their fins **10.** 100 **11.** Chew their food **12.** False **13.** Vegetables **14.** One metre wide **15.** Scales **16.** The North Atlantic Ocean **17.** Eels or sea snakes **18.** True **19.** 300 **20.** No – they lay eggs

Fun facts

Some sharks can smell small amounts of blood in the water from hundreds of metres away.

A blue shark was tagged in waters around New York. Sixteen months later it was recaptured in Brazilian waters, over 6000 kilometres away!

If a shark stops swimming it will slowly sink to the bottom of the ocean!

Q: Why didn't the shark bite the clown?

A: Because he tasted funny!

Wordsearch

FIN

GILLS

HUNTER

MEGALODON

SCALES

SHARK

SWIMMER

TAIL

TEETH

Can you find the words listed on the left, hidden in the wordsearch below?

S	W	I	M	M	E	R	F	E	O
R	H	O	S	C	A	L	E	S	I
T	L	A	D	H	L	R	F	W	T
A	T	C	K	U	A	S	I	U	E
I	A	G	R	N	D	R	E	L	E
L	O	I	G	T	H	N	K	G	T
S	E	L	T	E	T	U	M	A	H
T	K	L	L	R	E	S	A	F	J
F	C	S	R	D	O	T	F	I	G
M	E	G	A	L	O	D	O	N	U

PIRATES

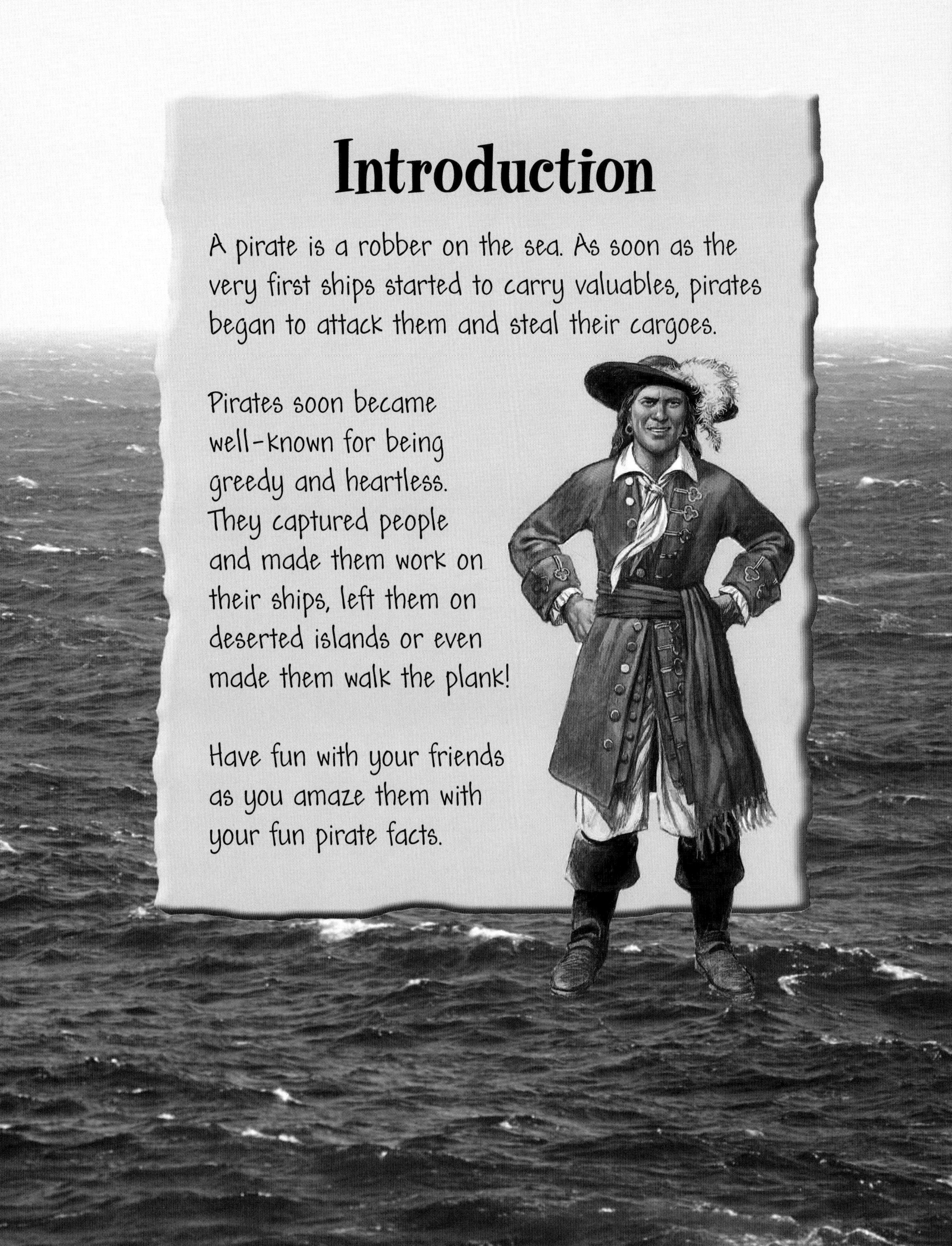

Introduction

A pirate is a robber on the sea. As soon as the very first ships started to carry valuables, pirates began to attack them and steal their cargoes.

Pirates soon became well-known for being greedy and heartless. They captured people and made them work on their ships, left them on deserted islands or even made them walk the plank!

Have fun with your friends as you amaze them with your fun pirate facts.

Mini stickers!

2 Find out all about the life of a pirate as you stick the mini stickers onto the chart below. Why did pirates bury their treasure? Who was the famous Black Bart? What was marooning and why was it done? Use your mini stickers to learn all about the most famous cut-throat pirates!

All at sea – Pirates had to survive for months aboard their ships, sometimes with little food or water

Famous pirates – Some pirates are still well-known for their terrible deeds even today

Pirate life – The Jolly Roger, treasure maps and pieces of eight were all part of everyday pirate life

Punishment – Any pirates who were caught were severely punished for breaking the law

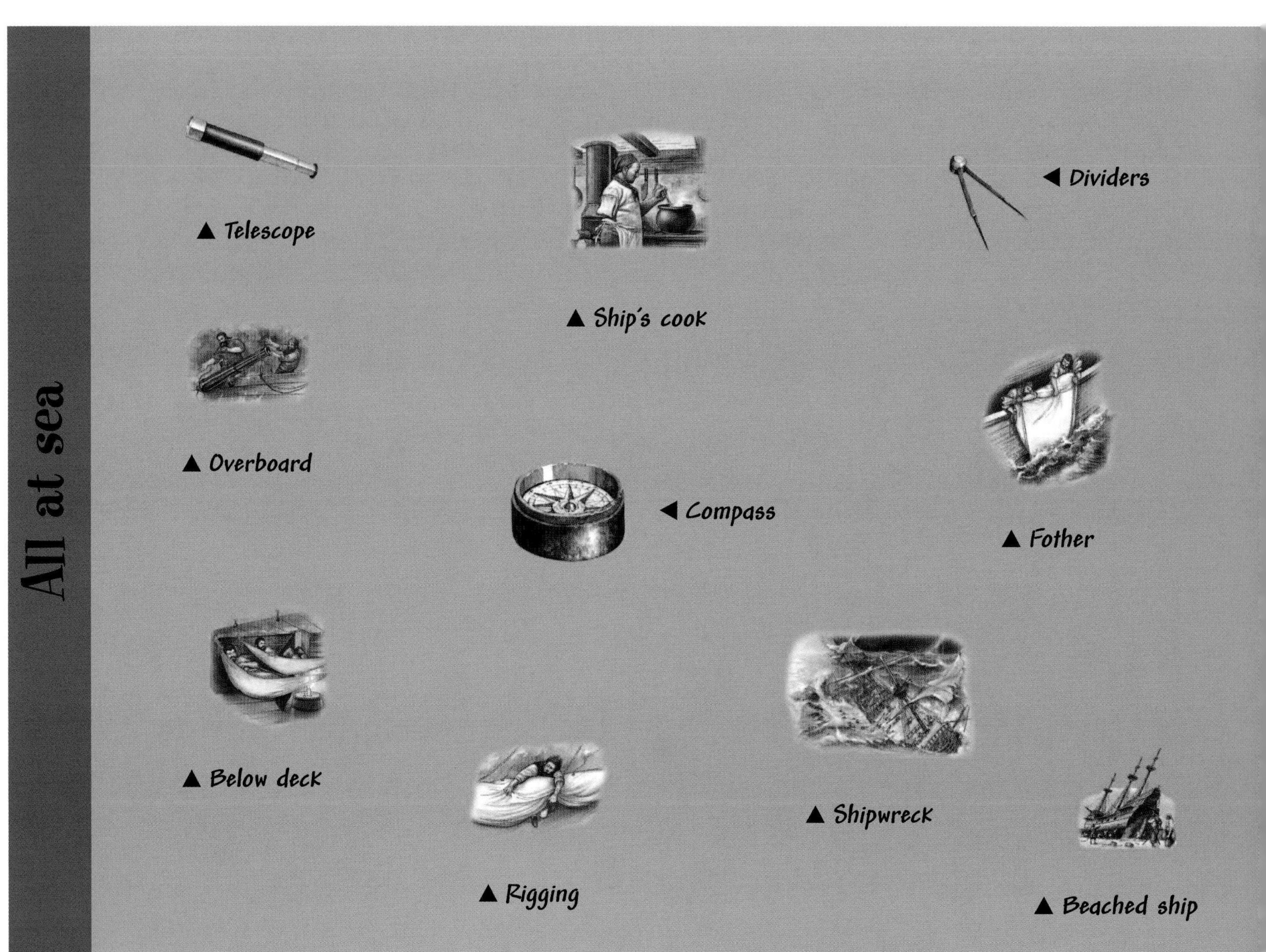

Famous pirates

▲ Black Bart

▲ Captain Hook

▲ Pirates of Penzance

▲ Grace O'Malley

◀ Francis L'Ollonais

▲ Henry Morgan

▲ Long John Silver

▲ William Kidd

▲ Barbarossa brothers

Pirate life

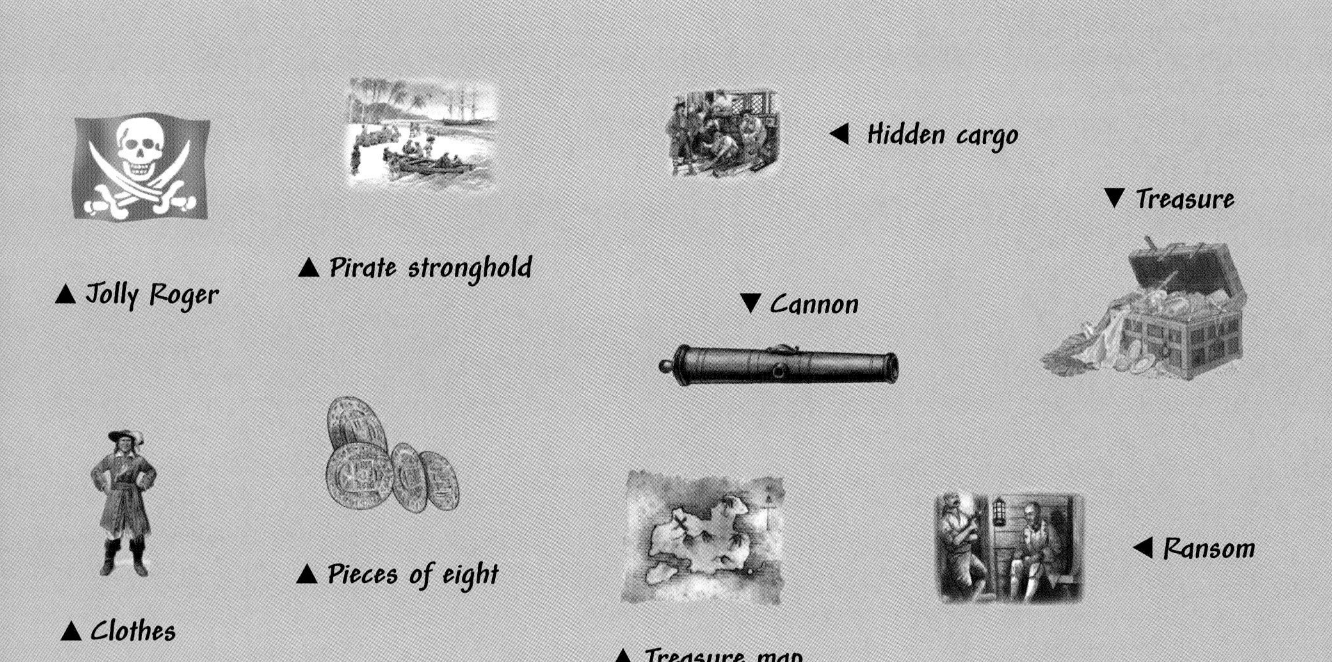

▲ Jolly Roger

▲ Pirate stronghold

◀ Hidden cargo

▼ Treasure

▼ Cannon

▲ Clothes

▲ Pieces of eight

▲ Treasure map

◀ Ransom

Punishment

▲ Pirate death

▲ Captured

▲ Prison

▲ Iron cage

Swash and buckle!

◄ Black Bart
Black Bart was a very successful pirate who captured over 400 ships in the 1720s

◄ Telescope
Pirates had to keep a careful look-out for other ships and be on their guard, ready to attack

◄ Pirate death
There was no code of conduct between pirates, they would steal from and murder each other too

◄ Below deck
Below deck it was very cramped and smelly so pirates spent as little time there as possible

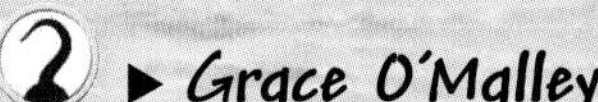

► Grace O'Malley
Women were sometimes pirates too – O'Malley went to sea as a young girl and ruled a group of pirates on the west coast of Ireland

► Hidden cargo
Merchants would hide their goods on board so pirates would hunt for the valuables

▼ Rigging
In bad weather the crew had to climb the rigging to alter the sails

◄ Treasure
Pirates stole what they could from other ships – sometimes the stolen loot was very valuable

KEY:

All at sea

Famous pirates

Pirate life

Punishment

▶ Henry Morgan

Morgan was a famous pirate who conquered Portobello in Cuba and Panama City

▶ Long John Silver

Silver is a one-legged pirate with a pet parrot who features in the book *Treasure Island*

▼ Captured

When pirates were captured they were chained together so that they could not escape

▼ Overboard

If a ship was in danger of running into rocks, anything heavy was thrown overboard so the ship would rise up out of danger

▲ Treasure map

Pirates kept a record of where they buried their treasure so they could return for it when it was safe

▶ Barbarossa brothers

The brothers were famous in the 1500s for their violent ways – they even attacked the pope's ship

◀ Compass

Pirates found their way at sea by using a compass

▲ Dividers

These were a useful tool that helped pirates to keep track of their route whilst they were at sea

'Barbarossa' was a nickname given to the brothers by their enemies because of the colour of their beards. Barba rossa means 'Redbeard' in Latin.

Shiver my timbers!

2 Women could be pirates too. Mary Read was taken prisoner by pirates and decided to join them in their search for treasure. Another woman pirate called Anne Bonny attacked Mary's ship. Instead of fighting they joined forces and became friends. They sailed the high seas together and became famous for their bravery.

▲ In a battle with the British navy the two women were brave and fought hard. Most of their male crew were scared and hid below deck, leaving the two women to fight alone!

All at sea

▲ Rigging

▲ Hidden cargo

▲ Black Bart

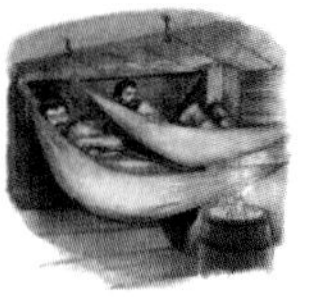
▲ Below deck

▲ Grace O'Malley

▲ Pirate death

▲ Telescope

▲ Treasure

▶ Pirate death

▲ Rigging

▶ Black Bart

▶ Treasure

◀ Grace O'Malley

▲ Below deck

▼ Telescope

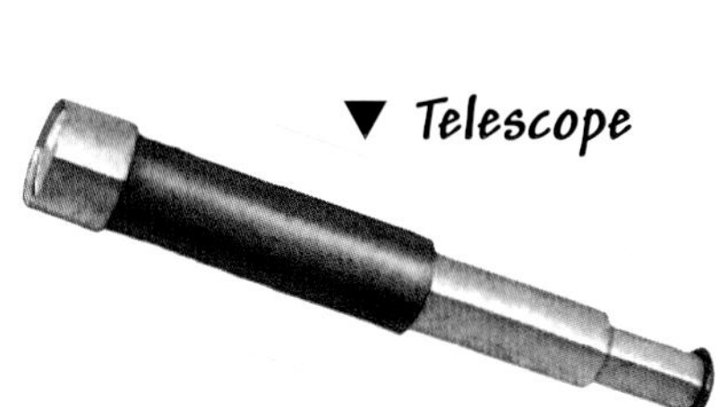

▲ Hidden cargo

All at sea

▲ Overboard

▲ Henry Morgan

▲ Long John Silver

▲ Treasure map

▲ Captured

▲ Barbarossa brothers

▲ Dividers

▲ Compass

▼ Henry Morgan

▼ Long John Silver

▶ Treasure map

▲ Captured

▶ Overboard

◀ Barbarossa brothers

▶ Compass

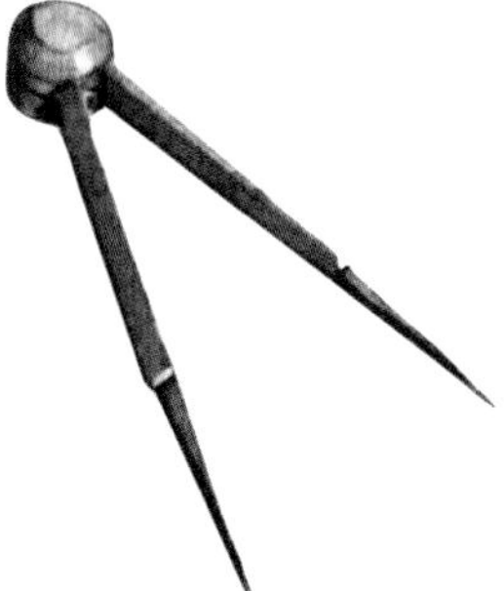

▲ Dividers

▼ Jolly Roger

▲ Ship's cook

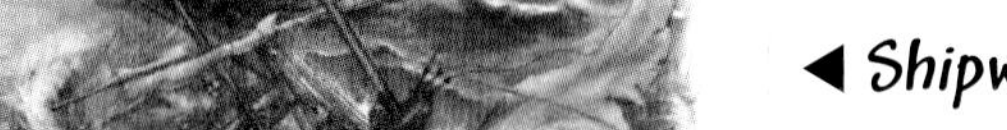

◀ Shipwreck

◀ Prison

▶ William Kidd

▲ Fother

◀ Francis L'Ollonais

▶ Clothes

▲ Ship's cook

▲ Jolly Roger

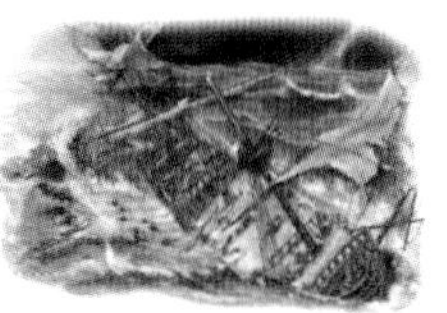

▲ Shipwreck

▲ Prison

▲ Fother

▲ William Kidd

▲ Clothes

▲ Francis L'Ollonais

All at sea

▼ Pieces of eight

▶ Beached ship

▶ Captain Hook

▼ Ransom

◀ Iron cage

▶ Pirate stronghold

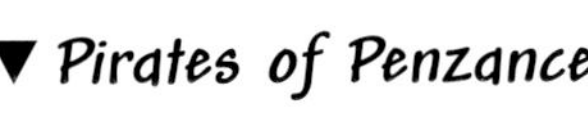

▼ Pirates of Penzance

▲ Cannon

▲ Beached ship

▲ Pieces of eight

▲ Captain Hook

▲ Ransom

▲ Iron cage

▲ Pirates of Penzance

▲ Pirate stronghold

▲ Cannon

Desert islands

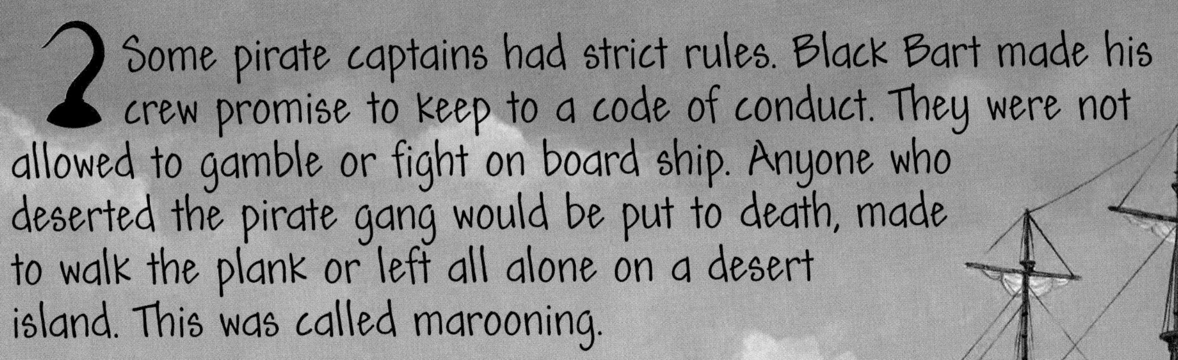

Some pirate captains had strict rules. Black Bart made his crew promise to keep to a code of conduct. They were not allowed to gamble or fight on board ship. Anyone who deserted the pirate gang would be put to death, made to walk the plank or left all alone on a desert island. This was called marooning.

The marooned pirate was left with a pistol and a little food and water. It was almost impossible to escape from desert islands, the only hope was to be picked up by a ship.

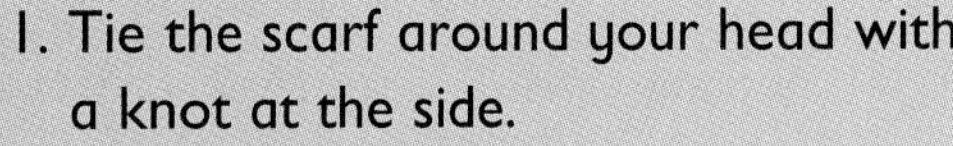

Dress like a pirate!

You will need:

• red scarf • bright trousers, shirt and waistcoat • long socks • black wool • cardboard • belt with buckle • scissors

1. Tie the scarf around your head with a knot at the side.
2. Next put on the bright trousers, shirt and waistcoat. Pull the long socks up over the bottoms of the trousers. Put the belt around your waist.
3. Carefully cut out a circle of card and thread the wool through it to make an eye patch.
4. Now all you need is a bloodcurdling pirate yell!

Swash and buckle!

◄ Ship's cook

Fresh food was rare on board ship, so the cook often had to serve dried biscuits and pickled meat

◄ Fother

A hole in the ship was sometimes patched with a sail, but it didn't hold for long, this was called fothering

▼ Jolly Roger

When a pirate captain decided to attack another ship he raised a special flag called the Jolly Roger

▼ Clothes

If pirates stole fine clothes they would often sell them, or if they liked them they would keep them for themselves

▲ Francis L'Ollonais

L'Ollonais was famous for his cruelty, so people surrendered as soon as they realized he was attacking them

◄ Prison

Before and after their trial, captured pirates were held in prisons such as Newgate Prison in London

► Shipwreck

Violent storms could spring up suddenly and wreck a ship with giant waves

▲ William Kidd

William Kidd started out as a pirate-hunter, but then became a pirate himself

KEY:

All at sea

Famous pirates

Pirate life

Punishment

▶ Beached ship

Pirates would drag their ship onto the beach so they could scrape off any barnacles and weeds

◀ Iron cage

Pirates who had been hanged were displayed in cages as a warning to other pirates

▼ Pirate stronghold

Sometimes pirates settled on land, and used it as a base to store their treasure

▲ Pieces of eight

These were the most famous pirate coins, and were about as big as a fifty pence piece – they were worth about £15 in today's money

▲ Ransom

Pirates would capture rich people and charge their family money to release them

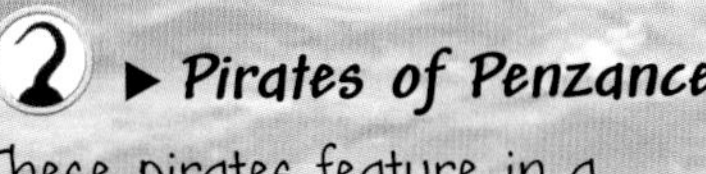

▶ Pirates of Penzance

These pirates feature in a famous operetta – but they are very kind-hearted so are not very realistic

▶ Captain Hook

This well-known pirate is Peter Pan's arch enemy

◀ Cannon

Cannons fired huge, heavy balls that would be shot at enemy ships to slow them down

The story of the famous and feared pirate Blackbeard was actually put on stage in 1798 as a ballet!

Pirate facts

Peter Pan cut off Captain Hook's hand and fed it to a crocodile, so the captain wore a hook instead.

Pirates also needed to steal everyday things. If they had been away from land for a long time they would take food, water and clothes.

Pirates in ancient times used small, fast boats with shallow bottoms so they could easily escape into shallow waters.

All aboard!

Read on to find out about more pirate antics

• Pirates would capture groups of people and make them work on board their ship. When they reached land the pirates made them work hard and treated them badly.

• Francis Le Clerc was a fierce pirate with a wooden leg. He captured the port of Havana and demanded money to let the people free. When they refused to pay he set fire to everything.

• Julius Caesar was captured by pirates when he was 25. While still a prisoner, he joked that he would come back and kill them all. In the end they released him, but he kept his promise and returned to kill them.

While she was a pirate, Grace O'Malley cut her hair short to look like her sailors. They gave her the nickname 'Baldy'!

Terror from the sea

Discover more about a pirate's life

• Pirates would attack other ships and slow them down by firing large cannon balls at their sails, so that the wind would no longer blow them along. This meant they could board the ships easily.

• Not every pirate flag was the famous skull-and-crossbones. Most early pirates used a bright red flag to frighten their victims. Pirates also added their own trademark symbols.

• Pirates didn't spend all of their time at sea. When they settled on land they set up camp, hunted for food and cooked over fires.

Pirate facts

The captain would share out the loot amongst his crew. He did this very carefully so that no one would complain.

Silk and porcelain were precious treasures from China. Pirates handled them carefully because they were so delicate.

Sometimes the crew would maroon their captain. They would turn against him if they felt he made bad decisions.

One of the most valuable cargoes of all were spices from India. They were difficult to sell so pirates simply dumped them overboard.

Test your memory!

The ship's cook was often a pirate who had been injured and so couldn't help above deck.

In calm weather there was little for the pirates to do. They would mend ropes and sails, or gamble with dice.

Pirates kept themselves well-armed. They used daggers and carried as many as six loaded pistols when attacking a ship.

How much can you remember from your pirate sticker activity book? Find out below!

1. Why didn't pirates spend much time below deck?
2. How many ships did Black Bart capture?
3. Where did pirates get their loot from?
4. Where did Grace O'Malley rule a group of pirates?
5. What was the name of the pirate brothers who were famous for their violence?
6. Which book does Long John Silver appear in?
7. How did pirates avoid their ship running into rocks?
8. What did pirates use dividers for?
9. Name two famous women pirates who were good friends.
10. Because fresh food was rare on board ship what foods did the pirates usually have?

Black Bart was probably the most successful pirate ever, yet he refused to drink anything stronger than tea!

11. What did the pirate captain do when he was about to attack another ship?

12. Name a famous prison in London where pirates were held.

13. What was fothering?

14. What was unusual about William Kidd?

15. Which book features Captain Hook?

16. Why would pirates drag their ship onto land?

17. Why aren't the Pirates of Penzance very realistic?

18. What was strange about Francis Le Clerc's leg?

19. Who was captured by pirates when he was 25?

20. What precious treasures came from China?

Answers:

1. It was cramped and smelly **2.** Over 400
3. They stole it from other ships **4.** Off the coast of Ireland
5. Barbarossa brothers **6.** *Treasure Island*
7. By throwing anything heavy overboard **8.** To navigate at sea
9. Mary Read and Anne Bonny **10.** Dried biscuits, pickled meat
11. He raised the pirate flag **12.** Newgate Prison
13. Fixing a hole in the boat with a sail
14. He started as a pirate-hunter but then became a pirate
15. *Peter Pan* **16.** To clean off barnacles and weeds
17. They are very kind-hearted **18.** It was wooden
19. Julius Caesar **20.** Porcelain and silk

Some people believe there is still pirate treasure to be found, buried on remote islands.

The play of *Peter Pan* featuring Captain Hook, is staged every Christmas in London.

The famous pirate Blackbeard made himself as scary as possible by plaiting ribbons in his beard and putting lighted matches in his hat!

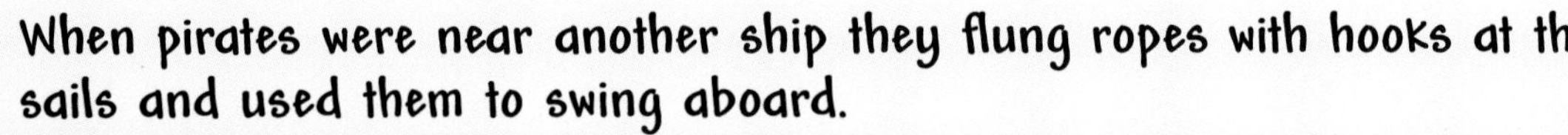

When pirates were near another ship they flung ropes with hooks at the sails and used them to swing aboard.

Wordsearch

Can you find the words listed on the left, hidden in the wordsearch below?

CANNON

CARGO

DECK

FLAG

PRISON

SHIPWRECK

TELESCOPE

TREASURE

VIKING

A	S	T	A	P	H	K	C	D	S
F	U	R	E	R	O	C	A	E	H
T	L	E	R	I	A	M	R	O	I
V	E	A	H	S	T	R	G	F	P
I	L	S	G	O	G	C	O	L	W
K	E	U	A	N	A	D	A	E	R
I	S	R	I	D	F	L	E	G	E
N	A	E	P	J	E	K	G	C	C
G	P	C	A	N	N	O	N	O	K
T	E	L	E	S	C	O	P	E	L